NICHOLAS DUNN

THE MAKING OF A TEXAS LEGEND

MARK GREATHOUSE

Nicholas Dunn: The Making of a Texas Legend

Copyright © 2020 Mark Greathouse
(Defiance Press & Publishing, LLC)

Printed in the United States of America

10 9 8 7 6 5 4 3 2 1

ISBN-13: 978-1-948035-70-5 (Paperback)
ISBN-13: 978-1-948035-71-2 (eBook)

Edited by Janet Musick
Cover designed by Spomenka Bojanic
Interior designed by Debbi Stocco

Published by Defiance Press and Publishing, LLC

Bulk orders of this book may be obtained by contacting Defiance Press and Publishing, LLC. www.defiancepress.com.

Public Relations Dept. – Defiance Press & Publishing, LLC
281-581-9300
pr@defiancepress.com

Defiance Press & Publishing, LLC
281-581-9300
info@defiancepress.com

The Kin of Kildare

By Mark Greathouse

'Twas the famine that drove them; thousands had died.
Ancestral kings and chieftains had e'er long gone.
The English took their bounty, but couldn't steal their pride.
Pixies danced, hobgoblins howled, and leprechauns laughed,
And the pride of Ireland stood fast.
And so it was with the kin of Kildare; did ya hear?
Five brothers left County Kildare for Texas one by one –
First Matthew, then Peter, John, Patrick, and Thomas –
The sons of Long Larry Dunn sailed forth to a promised land.
Lush live oak, pecan trees, and bluebonnets beckoned
Along the shores of Nueces Bay.
And so it was with these kin of Kildare; did ya hear?
They built their homes, tilled and ranched the land.
Their acreage knew no end, and their families flourished.
Years of starvation in Kildare replaced with a bountiful life;
Livestock bred aplenty; cotton, peaches, and plums all thrived.
God's bounty blessed them all.
And so it was with these kin of Kildare; did ya hear?
But the idyll succumbed to others' plans, as war and sin crept in.
Rustlers ambushed poor Larry; he never had a chance.
Christopher, Patrick, Joseph and more the yellow fever took,
Matthew murdered, defending his ranch from crazed drunken thieves.
This land took as much as it gave.
And so it was with these kin of Kildare; did ya hear?
Yet, these kinfolk of County Kildare, these staunch Irishmen endured.
They sowed and reaped and made life anew despite all the strife.
Their blood flows crimson in my children's veins,
And the green heathers of County Kildare will ever remember
The sons of Long Larry Dunn.
And so it was with these kin of Kildare; now ya hear.

DEDICATION

Dedicated to my family as a testament to the Irish-Texan heritage of my sons, Michael and Matthew, and to my loving wife, Carolyn.

LEGEND

An extremely famous or notorious person, especially in a particular field or endeavor; a person who inspires legends.

ACKNOWLEDGEMENTS

Special thanks to my Texas family for their contributions to this book, including my niece Heather Greathouse Wireman, nephew Shawn Greathouse, and cousins Jim and Cindy Holmgreen, Mary Bradley Kureska, Father Bob Dunn, Jan Tymrak, Johnny Dunn, Eddie Thornton, Arthur Kaler, Michael Meaney, Mitchell Thomas, and Mary Anne Bose. The support of friends is important, and I am grateful to Jim May, Chris Haug, Ernie Angell, Gene Blinn, Alan Bruzee, Dwighd Delgado, and Tom and Lisa Cantwell. Thanks also for the advice from journalist/novelist Murphy Givens and his Nueces Press publisher Jim Maloney.

I am especially thankful for Heather Siler and the great team at Defiance Press & Publishing, LLC for their encouragement and professionalism and to Cara Miller for introducing me to them. The team Defiance Press brings to publishing is first rate from promotion to editing, cover design, narration, and the myriad tasks that lead to successful book sales. Notably, it was the faith Defiance Press had in me and in my series of western historical fiction novels, The Tumbleweed Sagas, that fed the creative energies that refined "Nicholas Dunn: The Making of a Texas Legend."

Thanks to the legacy of my Great Uncle John Hillard Dunn for the hours he spent recording Dunn family adventures as they emigrated from Ireland and settled in South Texas. His written efforts provided the impetus that guided and inspired this humble author's work, which is an attempt to bring a portion of the history of South Texas to life through our family. Thanks especially to my loving dad, Jack Greathouse, for passing John's writings on to me. Special appreciation must extend to my Great Great Grandfather Nicholas Dunn, whose life inspired this riveting tale of a Texas family destiny. I humbly pray that I will have done justice to your memories.

I am also grateful to the written efforts of John Beamond "Red John" Dunn with his biographical work, the editing by his daughter Mary Maud Dunn Wright (pen name: Lilith Lorraine), and John W. Meaney for his writing and editing of an extensive three-volume family history.

While most of my own authoring occurred in my office, decorated to channel my inner Texan, my creative juices were often inspired in cafes and coffee houses. My favorites are Hester's Café & Coffee Bar in Corpus Christi, TX; Nueces Café in Robstown, TX; Java Ranch Espresso Bar & Café in Fredericksburg, TX; Ragged Edge Coffee House, 82 Café, and The Ugly Mug in Gettysburg, PA; and Frederick Coffee Company & Café, Baltimore Coffee Company, and Dublin Roasters in Frederick, MD. The décors and easy listening music combined with savory cups of coffee tended to set me in the right frame of mind.

Last but not least, authoring never occurs in a vacuum. I appreciate the connections I make as a member of the Western Writers of America; the myriad of valuable connections I make through social media; and the successful western genre authors who blaze the trails I humbly follow.

Thanks to all of you.

CONTENTS

THE CAST

*Dunn kinfolk highlighted in boldface play key roles in this story.

Ireland – The Dunn Family of County Kildare

Lawrence "Long Larry" Dunn (1775-1854). *Born: County Kildare, Ireland. Married Ellen O'Reilly (1779-1864), 1799. Dunn family patriarch. Farmer, teacher. Five sons: Patrick, John, Peter, Matthew, & Thomas.*

The Dunn Brothers Emigrate to Texas

Matthew Dunn (1809-1854). *Born: County Kildare, Ireland. Married Sarah Pritchett. Immigrated 1845. Farmer, sutler, soldier (fought in Mexican-American War) & rancher. Three sons: John B. "Red John", Matthew, & James.*

Patrick Dunn (1801-1899), *Born: County Kildare, Ireland. Married Ellen Wyse, later married Mary Anne Rogan. Immigrated 1868. Farmer. Nine children: Kate, Lawrence, Bridget, Mary, Liza, Thomas, Theresa, Anne, & Edward.*

John Dunn (1803-1889), *Born County Kildare, Ireland. Married Annie Hyland (1832-1867). Immigrated 1851. Farmer, cattleman, horse breeder. Nine children: Annie, John II, Michael, Joseph, Matthew, Patrick, Lawrence, Nicholas, & Christopher.*

Peter Dunn (1807-1890), *Born: County Kildare, Ireland. Married Margaret Maxwell (1812-1896). Immigrated 1850. Blacksmith. Eight children: Lawrence, Mary, Julia, Matthew, Joseph, Lucy, Judith, & Theresa.*

Thomas Dunn (1812-1863). *Born: County Kildare, Ireland. Married Catherine Hickey, 1826. Immigrated 1850. Farmer, merchant. Eight children: Lawrence, Andrew, Michael, Joseph, Thomas, Catherine, Patrick, & Mary.*

Dunn Brothers' Children Key to Texas Story

Nicholas Dunn (1835-1912), *Born: County Kildare, Ireland. Son of John & Annie Dunn. Married Andree Ann Goebel (1846-1929) (var. Andree Ann Gable). Immigrated 1850 with his Uncle Peter. Cattleman, marksman, horse breeder, speculator, Indian fighter. Nine children: Ellender "Nellie", Annie, Michael, Agnes, John Francis, Dominic, Margaret "Maggie", Mary, & Teresa.*

John Francis Dunn (1870-1948), *Born: Corpus Christi, TX. Son of Nicholas & Andree Ann Goebel Dunn. Married Margaret Crain (1887-1974). Rancher, Texas Ranger, banker. Five children: John F. II, James, Mary Anne, William, & Robert.*

Matthew Dunn (1841-1868), *Born: County Kildare, Ireland. Son of John & Annie Dunn. Married Mary Ann. Immigrated 1851 with his father. Cattleman, rancher.*

Michael Dunn (1848-1921), *Born: County Kildare, Ireland. Son of John & Annie Dunn. Married Catherine Whelan (1855-1903). Immigrated 1851 with his father. Cattleman, rancher. Twelve children: John H., Michael, Nellie, Edmund, Annie, Leo, Christopher, Lawrence, Nora, Mary, Joseph, and Katie.*

Lawrence Dunn (1837-1864), *Born: Corpus Christi, TX. Son of John & Annie Dunn. Cattleman, soldier.*

John "Red John" Dunn (1851-1946), *Born: Corpus Christi, TX. Son of Matthew Dunn (son of Long Larry Dunn). Entrepreneur, Texas Ranger, militiaman, museum curator. Two children: John & Maude.*

John Hillard Dunn (1883-____), *Born: Corpus Christi, TX. Son of Michael & Katherine Dunn. Married Stella Grissom. Entrepreneur, railroad grading, Panama Canal construction, roadmaster on Nickel Plate Railroad, Dunn Grocery Co. Three children: Michael, John, & Estelle.*

Patrick F. Dunn (1858-1937), *Born: Corpus Christi, TX. Son of Thomas (son of Long Larry Dunn) & Catherine Dunn. Married Clara Brown (1857-1910). Rancher (Padre Island). Three children: May, Lalla, & John Burton.*

HISTORICAL CHARACTERS

General Zachary Taylor (1784-1850) – *Victorious U.S. Army general during Mexican-American War, 1845-1848, Twelfth president of the United States, 1850.*

Colonel Henry Lawrence Kinney (1814-1862) – *Established trading post that became Corpus Christi, encouraged settlement, motivated Matthew Dunn to send to Ireland for his four brothers. Killed in gunfight in Mexico in 1862.*

Sam Houston – *One of the most illustrious leaders of Texas. Led Texas independence and served as first president of the Republic of Texas, U.S. senator, and Texas governor.*

General Antonio Lopez de Santa Anna – *Thanks to epic blunders, lost Battle of San Jacinto to Texans in 1836; defeated by U.S. General Scott at Buena Vista, Mexico in 1848.*

Také-vera – *Comanche chief.*

Costalites – *Lipan Apache chief, allied with Mescalero Apache and later with Comanche. Mostly fought Mexicans.*

Juan Nepomuceno "Cheno" Cortina – *Mexican rancher, politician, military leader, outlaw, and folk hero who did not accept the terms of the Treaty of Guadalupe-Hidalgo and fought against settlers, U.S. soldiers, and Texas Rangers on the Nueces Strip.*

Leander McNelly, Ben McNelly, John Coffee Hays, Rip Ford, & Matthew Caldwell – *Famous Texas Ranger leaders.*

NICK DUNN'S FAMILY TREE

Lawrence "Long Larry" Dunn* & Ellen O'Reilly

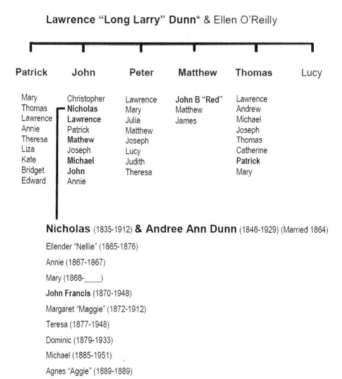

Patrick	John	Peter	Matthew	Thomas	Lucy
Mary	Christopher	Lawrence	**John B "Red"**	Lawrence	
Thomas	**Nicholas**	Mary	Matthew	Andrew	
Lawrence	**Lawrence**	Julia	James	Michael	
Annie	Patrick	Matthew		Joseph	
Theresa	**Mathew**	Joseph		Thomas	
Liza	Joseph	Lucy		Catherine	
Kate	**Michael**	Judith		**Patrick**	
Bridget	**John**	Theresa		Mary	
Edward	Annie				

Nicholas (1835-1912) **& Andree Ann Dunn** (1846-1929) (Married 1864)

Ellender "Nellie" (1865-1876)

Annie (1867-1867)

Mary (1868-____)

John Francis (1870-1948)

Margaret "Maggie" (1872-1912)

Teresa (1877-1948)

Dominic (1879-1933)

Michael (1885-1951)

Agnes "Aggie" (1889-1889)

*Names in boldface type are featured in this story.

MAP OF SOUTH TEXAS

1845-1912

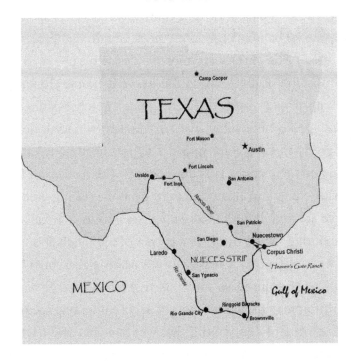

JUST SAYIN'

How hot was it? I could have pan-fried an egg on a rock. But the heat was eased just a tad by a warm gentle breeze out of the northwest. The sweat-soaked bandana round my neck caught that breeze and had a cooling effect. The skies were mostly crystal clear – an azure blue that was almost impossible to describe – save for some clouds working themselves up in the distance. There wasn't much besides grass, an occasional cypress, and a few live oak mottes 'round these parts, so you could pretty much see for miles. The prairie stretched far off into the horizon and then some. This day – now – I'd thank God for such a clear unobstructed view. It was a far cry from the rolling green heather of my native Ireland, but I had already grown to love Texas.

I was scouting the far northwest corner of my ranch about 40 miles or so due west of Corpus Christi. It was a fair-sized spread, and my longhorn beeves required as much as five acres each. I was feeling pretty comfortable in the saddle, sort of accommodating the heat. Now and then, I'd wipe my brow with that wet bandana and try to take in whatever breeze I could catch. Folks usually travelled in pairs in these parts, but I had sent my *vaquero* Jorge home earlier and figured I'd just spend another couple of hours looking for our cattle before turning back. Besides, that northwest breeze portended some nasty weather by day's end. Texas weather was changeable, to say the least. There we were, just me and the big roan I was riding. As was common, I avoided the high grasses and followed a dry creek bed. I just happened to ease past a motte with a few live oak trees.

I froze! The hair rose on the back of my neck.

There were three or four of what looked like Comanche at least a half mile out. I slipped the Sharps .50 caliber carbine from its scabbard and slid from my saddle. I coaxed the big roan to lie down ever so gently, and we hid behind the natural cover of the live oak motte. I untied my bedroll, laid it over the roan's quivering body, and slipped the Sharps inside the fold of the blanket to avoid the sun's reflection on the barrel. It wouldn't do to be giving my position away by some inadvertent flash of sunlight. I pointed it in the general direction of the Comanche. The roan stirred. I gently patted his neck to keep him steady. It was so quiet, I could just about hear the tree grow. If the Comanche did come after me, I expected my pistol, my trusty Colt, would be handier in these close quarters than the Sharps. Besides, they'd likely circle round and come at me from behind. Hopefully, I'd hear them before I saw them.

The breeze coming toward me out of the northwest was a blessing, as it tended to muffle sound and carry any tell-tale scents away from the Comanche. It's good to be downwind in these sorts of situations. I could only hope they hadn't heard me – or seen me.

They were outfitted in full war regalia so far as I could tell, though I wasn't about to take another peek to be certain. Comanche on the warpath generally painted their faces with one or more broad black horizontal stripes, though they were known to use other colors. From the small size of the party, they were likely scouts from a larger band and looking for folks wandering about like myself. I was pretty sure they were in fact Comanche, as I heard they'd been active in the region of late. In any case, these Comanche were about a day's ride from my home. There was no telling what might be on the Comanche minds. It sure didn't look like they were hunting game.

It wasn't that long ago, around 1840, that a Penateka Comanche chief named Buffalo Hump had torn up much of Texas to Victoria and Linnville right on down to the Gulf shores. He'd burned and pillaged unmercifully with a band of what was estimated at the time to number a thousand warriors. I was blessed to have come to Texas a decade after that terrible attack. Many folks saw it as the last life gasp of the Comanche. But, fact was, the Comanche were still around these parts, as evidenced by the group I was trying to avoid attracting the attention of.

The reputation the Comanche had for tortures inflicted on their prisoners rivaled the British treatment of many of my countrymen. I'd seen the British do terrible things but definitely didn't want to experience whatever the Comanche conjured up. I wondered if the Comanche and British might have colluded on tortures at some point but figured it was more just the inbred evil that some folks seemed born with. It's hard to get a grip on man's inhumanity to man.

There's a romanticized image of the Comanche as some sort of noble savage. Actually, they had mostly pretty scrawny physiques, but they made up for it by their remarkable horsemanship. Plus, it was said they could shoot a dozen arrows while hanging from a pony in the time it took to reload a flintlock rifle. No question they were fierce warriors. Engaging Comanche was akin to plunging yourself into a nest of rattlesnakes. Didn't matter which one bit you; you were going to die.

I stayed crouched down behind the roan stallion, the carbine nestled in that blanket. I didn't move a muscle. All my senses were on high alert. Every now and then a mosquito or fly would hover round, but I didn't dare swat at them. I barely felt the warm ever-so-gentle breeze, breathed in the leathery smell of my tack, heard the nervous breathing of my horse, and occasionally wiped away the salty beads of sweat around my eyes. I yearned for the canteen on the other side of the roan but dared not risk further motion or noise. Now and then, the stallion would give a sort of muffled snort, and I could only pray we hadn't been heard. To make matters worse, I was on the sunny side of that live oak motte such that I could just as easily have been crouched in an oven. 'Bout this time, those clouds way off in the distance had worked up a bit of a threat. Shards of lightning didn't bode well. I didn't need rain and flash flooding complicating my situation.

I heard the Comanche talking as they came a bit closer. Their voices tended to carry toward me with the breeze. Of course, I couldn't understand a lick of what they were saying, and some of it was sign language anyway. For a few brief moments, the sound seemed to get even closer before they apparently shifted direction away from my position and their voices began to trail off. I prayed that they weren't following the meandering creek bed I was hiding beside. I knew it carved a wide arc between my position and the Comanche. It was a typical Nueces Strip landscape. It was also known as the Wild Horse Desert, owing to millions of mustangs roaming across its prairies. It encompassed south Texas from Uvalde and the Nueces River to the Rio Grande. My ranch was in the region well west of Corpus Christi and transitioning to the sparser grasses and sandy loam soil that becomes escarpments of caliche hills well to my west. It might be described as the mother of the great cattle herds that numbered in the hundreds of thousands throughout South Texas. Yep…the land of the longhorn.

It seemed like ages as the Comanche took their sweet time to mosey on. I placed my hand on the big roan's withers to steady him as I slowly arose from my crouched position. I couldn't see any Comanche, but that wasn't to say they'd left the area. They could be spitting distance from me, and I wouldn't know it. By now, my horse was standing again. He shook off what must have been at least an hour hunkered down in the heat beside those live oaks.

Just when I thought I might be in the clear, a javelina trotted across the creek bed. I held my breath as it stopped for a moment and eyed me before moving along. The javelina were nasty, smelly wild pigs that were indigenous to the region. The last thing I needed was to have to shoot the dang thing. Such a sound with Comanche anywhere nearby would surely have spelled trouble.

I led the roan at a slow easy walk, figuring to backtrack a few hundred yards along the creek bed and keep a low profile before remounting. I held the carbine at the ready and once again checked that the .44 caliber Colt Walker revolver on my hip was ready to go into action. If those Comanche came after me, they'd eat plenty of lead. It was no surprise that folks on the frontier – especially Texas Rangers – referred to the Colt as "The Difference." In fact, Samuel Colt's invention had been perfected on advice of a Texas Ranger named Sam Walker and had taken the measure of many a marauding hostile. I slowly and quietly eased back along that creek bed, pausing every now and then to scan the horizon.

I'm reminded that we venture out into the prairie by twos for our own protection, though in this case being alone made it less likely that I'd have been spotted. Such were the dangers we faced out here in South Texas in the 1850s. Notably, fighting Indians wasn't always about shooting; often it was about avoiding confrontation. It was about keeping your hair.

I've heard that I'm reputed to be a pretty fair marksman, an Indian fighter, a decent drover, and a rancher and cattle speculator of some success. I've striven to be a good husband and father. My name is Nicholas Dunn. From the depths of my beating Irish heart born of the gentle green fields and oak forests of Killeigh in County Kildare on February 12, 1835, I offer you my story. Mine is a story of escaping the potato famine and religious persecutions by the British that raged through Ireland in the 1840s and enduring the hardships and dangers of the South Texas frontier to ultimately carve out a life of peace, love, and happiness. I arrived in Texas in 1850 with two of my uncles. Mine is a story of family destiny, of opportunity, of indomitable will. May the spirit of Ireland ever live in the annals of the Dunn family of Kildare and their descendants in Texas and the United States of America.

I was the second of nine children of John Dunn and my dear mother, the former Annie Hyland. If you were to imagine the prototypical Irishman, it would be me with my red hair, twinkling blue eyes set in a broad face, stocky muscular build, and fair complexion. And yes, I had my complement of freckles. It was sort of ironic that the name Dunn means brown-haired. Red hair? Must have been a touch of Viking blood in our ancestry. As I matured, it was said that I became an unforgettable character for all who knew me. I'll assume that unforgettable is a good characteristic. I'd eventually earn a reputation as being tough yet fair. However, I think it was my grandfather Lawrence "Long Larry" Dunn who instilled a true spirit of adventure in me. It was likely embedded in my soul by the way I was raised, but I have always loved God, people, life, and freedom. I'll let you be the judge as I share my tale, as interwoven with that of my family.

As you read, try to transport yourself to a place peopled by true pioneers, a mostly uncharted land featuring rather rudimentary, even primitive conditions. Violence in Texas was ubiquitous, ethnic bitterness a constant, weapons and tactics basic, and lawlessness characterized by thievery and killings all too common. Yet this was counterbalanced by a commitment to family and community, coupled with a love for life, faith in God, and an enduring desire to build a productive life in South Texas. Land was king, as money really wasn't worth much.

In my humble estimation, we Texans were and ever will be a fiercely independent lot. While we generally distrust government and the inevitable march of people from the East, we also embraced it as a direct agency to do the bidding of the people for protection and otherwise shaping their destiny. Importantly, the ideas and ambitions of those who opened the frontier played an ever-increasing role in shaping America.

Texas represented but one of a series of frontiers seeming to appear and disappear with a sort of magic as various sections of the nation were revealed to enterprising settlers. As I've said, there was violence even worse than the dime novels, but it was never glorified for its own sake. We saw past all that. The lure of low-cost land and a better future for our families constantly drew folks seeking that better life or, failing that, a more adventurous one. You might call them "second chancers." With its allure, South Texas was no exception.

Oh, now, mind you that I don't truck with embellishment. No, not me. Some folk think we Irish tend to exaggerate. What I share with you is true...as I remember it. No blarney.

To truly and fully appreciate the toughness, loyalty, faith, and determination that characterized the Dunn family in South Texas, I think that a necessarily brief consideration of Ireland of the 1840s is important toward establishing the backdrop – the context, if you will – that produced and inspired the likes of my grandfather Long Larry Dunn and his progeny – my father and my uncles. I couldn't begin to do any full Irish history justice here, so urge you to read some of the fine books on the subject. Long Larry was a well-read man; he enthusiastically and earnestly – as I've said – shared his knowledge with those around him, whether family or friends or any who might listen.

As is often the case, it is the confluence of particular events that drives the future, and so it is that a convergence of events roughly 4,700 miles apart drives this saga of the children – and grandchildren – of Long Larry Dunn. It's my story.

The 1840s were an especially difficult time in Ireland. The potato famines scourged the land, and most harvested crops were shipped to England. It helps to understand that potatoes – more easily grown in a rocky soil – were a food crop, while grains like oats and barley were considered a cash or income crop. The potato blight, combined with all manner of human atrocities perpetrated by British Queen Victoria's cruel, heavy-handed landlords and overseers, meant that each day brought ever more desperation among Irish citizenry. It was no exception for my grandfather Long Larry Dunn's family.

Then, that confluence of events that I mentioned occurred. In 1845, General Zachary Taylor was in Corpus Christi, Texas preparing for the likelihood of doing battle with Mexico. The reasons for the war were debated, but the fact remains that it happened. It coincided with the annexation of Texas by the United States and was precipitated after attacks by Mexican troops on American forces just north of the Rio Grande. Congress declared war.

Famine, oppression, war, and opportunity. What a strange yet fortuitous confluence of events indeed. No surprise that hardship bred strong, hardy men. And there were plenty of men to be found.

By the mid-1840s, thousands of my countrymen were fleeing Ireland to escape the famine and British persecution. We popists, as we were called for following the Pope, were oppressed as followers of Rome rather than the Church of England. At that, we were considered "black" Catholics, owing to St. Patrick having been judged to have corrupted Catholicism with pagan beliefs to more easily convert the Irish centuries ago. Despite such gut-wrenching cultural difficulties, I hope you might appreciate how hard it was to leave the wondrous rolling green hills and verdant forests of Ireland, to leave behind centuries of heritage. So it was that my Uncle Matthew came to the United States in 1845 to join General Zachary Taylor's army as a sutler and teamster and to settle near Corpus Christi, Texas. His four brothers – including my father, John – would follow and, by 1868, all would be settled along the Nueces Strip near Corpus Christi. Thus, it is at this juncture of time where my life story – my Texas story – begins. As I share my story, my family's story, I pray that you will understand how my Irish heritage was intricately woven into my life. Oh, and I'm not an Irish-Texan…I'm a Texan. That was a given the moment I set foot in Corpus Christi.

ONE

Coming to America

If you're lucky enough to be Irish, you're lucky enough!
Old Irish Saying

The Dunn story in South Texas – my story – begins with my Uncle Matthew. Uncle Matthew's journey to America was less about escaping an Ireland fraught with persecution and famine and far more about embarking on a new life filled with anticipated opportunities. Most of what I share with you about my dear uncle is from what he wrote about in letters and told me directly when I eventually joined him in South Texas.

Flat...humid...hot. At first look, seemingly not fit for man nor beast. A far cry from the Emerald Isle. It was 1845, and my Uncle Matthew found himself in Corpus Christi on the Gulf coast of Texas. He'd landed in New Orleans and found passage to the fast-growing port city. Matthew had responded to a call for settlers from Colonel Henry Kinney, who'd established a trading post that became Corpus Christi. There was no shortage of opportunity to carve out a life in the vast reaches of the Nueces Strip extending westward.

Upon arrival in Corpus Christi, Matt started his Texas life out as a storekeeper, a sutler supplying the army. That worked out while the troops were stationed in the United States, but he then learned that, as a civilian, he would not be able to accompany the troops into Mexico. In order to be eligible, he had to enlist in the army as a teamster. Apparently, he could not join the regular army, as they weren't accepting raw – that is, untrained – recruits. Of note, at age 36 he was already proficient in the use of a rifle, despite the prohibitions on firearms enforced by the British occupiers in Ireland. While plows and hoes were his tools of the farming trade, he was handy with the ancient claymore, as well. The claymore, by the way, is one nasty sword and Irish youth were trained in its use at an early age. As Uncle Matt would later tell me, the irony of being a "raw recruit" was not lost on him. And, in case you're wondering, I can handle a claymore, too.

To more fully understand what drove us to leave our home country, let's first set the stage for Uncle Matthew's journey to Texas by backing up just a few months. What I'm going to relate to you here was what I overheard at Dunn family gatherings and learned from first-hand experience.

Back in County Kildare where we all lived, Matthew Dunn tilled the land and reaped its bounty. He raised potatoes, just about enough to feed himself and eke out a living despite the British occupiers carving out their prodigious share of cash crops. But, just as his countrymen experienced, he found that farming was a bare subsistence. A significant portion of the Irish population lived in poverty and subsisted on naught but potatoes. It tended to keep them economically depressed as well. The gap between life and death was quite narrow. Fortunate were those who raised oats and barley, as these were considered "cash crops" by Her Majesty. Unfortunately, the cash crops were mostly exported, leaving the Irish mostly destitute. In a way, my uncle was fortunate that he had no wife and children to feed and clothe. Moreover, by virtue of what was called the Cottier system, England managed to demand and maintain cheap labor to keep the Irish in servitude. It made for a living, but hardly a life.

Then, the potato crops failed and famine struck. The blight began quite mysteriously in the late summer of 1845, as leaves on potato plants all of a sudden turned black and curled, then rotted. What a horror it was to watch family livelihoods disappear with their decaying crops. The potato rot phenomenon appeared to have occurred soon after a dense fog had swept across the fields of Ireland. Little did anyone know at the time, but the fog carried an airborne fungus that was said to have been originally transported in the holds of cargo ships traveling from Mexico to North America and thence to England. Winds wafting in from southern England – Wales, if you must know – had carried the fungus and permeated the Irish countryside. Little remained untouched. They called the fog a miasma.

The blight spread rapidly throughout the fields as fungal spores settled on the leaves of healthy potato plants and then were carried to surrounding plants. The attacked plants fermented, providing the nourishment the fungus needed to thrive and releasing a sickening smell as the plants died before the disbelieving eyes of Irish farmers. Past crops had failed due to weather and other diseases, but this was quite different. Even potatoes pulled from the ground ahead of the blight at first looked edible, but shriveled and rotted within days, having been attacked by the same fungus.

Matt was frightened at what the future might hold and whether this seemingly God-wrought crop disease could possibly be overcome. Worse still, the British were exacting their potato "tax" on any remaining healthy crops. The rest of the Dunn family was no less affected by this disaster, and there were the beginnings of reports of Irish families going hungry and even dying of starvation in the farms near Dublin. Counties Offaly, Kildare, and Wexford wouldn't be far behind. The Dunns feared for their children and for themselves.

On a crisp late August day, Matt witnessed one of his best friends, Edmund Connell, being flogged by a British overseer for having not delivered his required share of potatoes. Through teeth clenched in pain, Connell pleaded that he needed just a wee little of his crop to feed his family. To look at the already wasting bodies of his wife and three young children, one would have expected even some small mercy from the Lord Overseer. Instead, he redoubled his strokes. Connell's back, lean as it was from malnourishment, was hideously crossed with cuts and welts.

"There, let that be a lesson, wretch!" he growled, and then kicked Connell away from the flogging post. He looked over at Matt and gave him a snarling toothless grimace, as though he might be next.

Matt avoided eye contact, turned, and trudged home, never looking back. The leering face of the Lord Overseer was embedded on his mind. He pushed open the door to his cottage, hung up his hat, and uncharacteristically slumped into the big chair before the fireplace. He didn't stoke the fire. He felt lonely and unfulfilled. A sense of adventure lurking within his breast yearned to be set free. Might the British and the potatoes do the trick?

Matt's expression reflected a combination of despair born of hopelessness and fear of the unknown. He muttered to himself, "It's not enough that the queen's cruel overseers treat us as chattel and rip away our livelihood." He considered his brothers, who seemed intent on enduring the pestilence that destroyed crops, and the suffering inflicted by the Brits and their toadies, but…

Matt pulled out the well-worn clipping from his pocket. "It is time," he thought. "It is time indeed." The newspaper advertisement was a call for Irishmen to come to America to escape the famine and the British. He need only volunteer to support the army, and he'd be pretty much guaranteed land and lodging in the idyllic Nueces River Valley around a place in Texas called Corpus Christi. It was time to begin a new life, a free life in America. It sounded incredibly promising and would certainly fulfill his yearning for freedom and adventure. The confluence of events had come together for the Dunn family.

Matt knew that telling his father would be the toughest task. Long Larry Dunn was first and ever foremost a Catholic and a close second to that was his love of his family. Any parting could be expected to hurt deeply.

However, it would be eased a bit by the fact that Matt had already hinted to his father what he had been considering. The ravaged crops and increased persecution by the British had spawned many family conversations. This decision would actually be not so great a surprise. Long Larry had shared many inspiring stories of Irish history and the adventures of their ancestors. He instilled a sort of fire in the belly in his sons to be freedom-loving, independent, hardy souls who could endure life's toughest challenges with strength and grace.

In his heart, my grandfather sensed that his son Matt would be followed all too soon by his other sons and their children. It would bring him a paradoxical combination of pride, sadness, and joy.

Long Larry, as his name implied, was a tall man, long of frame. Hearing his stories, I always sensed an unresolved spirit of adventure in my grandfather. Had he been born a few generations earlier, he might have fought with the rebels against the British. Or, he could as easily have joined his ancestors marauding across the North Sea. Little wonder, then, that his stories instilled a sense of adventure, of wanderlust, in his sons and grandchildren.

But back to Matt's story. The next afternoon, he headed off to see Long Larry, to the house he had grown up in. Fond memories permeated every nook and cranny…the yard where he chased goats and chickens…the tree he would climb to hide and avoid chores…the thatched roof he'd jumped from…years of memories.

Long Larry was sitting on the front stoop whittling some sort of ornament. When he saw Matt approaching, he took a deep breath and put away his whittling knife. He glanced over his shoulder, "Ellen," he almost whispered, "Ellen, I think we're about to get some news."

"Well, come in, and I'll make tea." She knew that tea had a soothing effect on Long Larry.

They went inside, and Matt soon followed.

Now understand that I was there witnessing all of this, because my father had sent me to borrow some steel rasps to sharpen the blade of our scythe. I was a mere ten years old but already filled with wanderlust. Uncle Matt nodded to me as he strode up, paused, and gave me just a wee bit of a wistful smile as he entered the house. I sensed a tear in the corner of his right eye.

They had barely seated themselves at the big rough-hewn oaken table that dominated the sitting room when my grandfather offered the obvious, "So, dear son of mine, you've come to tell us that you're going to America." He'd lost his light-hearted Irish lilt, yet there was no sadness in his tone.

"Aye, Father. With the potatoes dyin' and the Brits persecuting our people, I yearn to leave, to seek new opportunity." As he showed his father the rumpled old advertisement, Matt saw the resignation in his father's normally lively eyes. "It's a new land with new opportunities." He knew it wouldn't be quite that simple. "'Tis said that land can be had almost for the asking."

"Matthew Dunn, we love you dearly," Long Larry sighed, trying to dig deep for his Irish spirit. He knew his son well enough to know that he'd planned this move in great detail. He tilted his head and forced a smile. "Well, let's be sure you have all you need." He looked resignedly at my grandmother. "Perhaps we can visit you in this Texas place." It was as though he knew that would never happen.

I could hardly wait to get home and tell my father what I had learned. I ran as fast as my legs would carry me. This was big news, and word of Matt's decision would travel quickly to the rest of the family as well as to friends. Still, they had to be careful, as the British Lord Overseers could make life miserable and otherwise delay Matt's move.

As for me, having seen the advertisement and heard Matt's story about great opportunity in Texas, it began to create a longing inside my own soul for the adventure such a move might hold. I was not optimistic about my future there in Kildare.

I recall standing on the dock a mere three weeks after Uncle Matt's announcement. The ship he boarded would take him to Liverpool and thence to New Orleans. It was a cloudy day but hope and promise lingered in the brisk damp Irish air. With a mix of sadness and envy, I watched the sails of Matt's ship disappear over the horizon. Long Larry had come to see his son off and wish him Godspeed. As the ship sailed out of sight, my grandfather caught my far-off gaze. He looked down at me and stared deeply into my eyes. "Aye, dear Nicholas, there be you soon enough, methinks." He seemed to sense the wanderlust already building within me. We walked to the carriage with his arm draped fondly over my shoulder. He muttered something about family and destiny.

"Do you truly think my destiny will be in Texas, Grandfather?"

Long Larry smiled a knowing smile. "Lad, you are growing up. You are a bright lad strengthened by your faith in God. There is a spirit in you that begs to be lived. You won't be happy here in Kildare knowing of the opportunities that could be yours in America." He seemed resigned to the fate of his family. "Your father and uncles won't be far behind your Uncle Matt, my boy." He was resigned but happy. "But they will live free of British shackles."

My Uncle Matt had stirred indescribable visions within me. The embers of longing for adventure had been stoked and were just beginning to catch fire. It wouldn't be long.

TWO

War

A true Texan would charge into hell with a bucket of ice water.

Texas-ism

To set the stage for my own eventual immigration to Texas, I feel it's important to describe my Uncle Matt's experiences. Of course, his letters always described Texas as a sort of land of milk and honey. He didn't share the tougher side of his experiences until I'd already arrived in Corpus Christi. Thus, in describing Matt's life before my own immigration, I'm going to jump just a little ahead of sharing my own reasons for leaving Ireland.

As he shared with me a few years later, Uncle Matt's trip across the Atlantic took about three months. Their sailing ship was buffeted heavily by at least one storm, but he endured. My uncle had brought a bare minimum of what he considered essentials – a bed, small wardrobe, writing desk, farming and cooking implements, a chest full of clothes – to establishing a life in his soon to be adopted country. Blessedly, all of his belongings arrived intact, no small feat given the circumstance of the voyage. While he'd only brought what he felt was practical, there were emotional considerations as well. These things served as a connection with his Irish roots, with family. They would serve to conjure and reinforce memories of the familiar world he'd left behind, while he also saw them as links from the past to the future.

According to Matt, the boat voyage from New Orleans to Corpus Christi, along the coast comprised mostly of barrier islands, was uneventful. The newness of it all was overwhelming. He was excited yet fearful. Upon setting foot on the pier in Corpus Christi, Matt knelt and prayed for God's blessing on his future in this new land of opportunity. I can only imagine what a relief it was just to be on solid land. Later, I would be better able to appreciate that feeling of joy and relief through my own experience.

Texas was about to join the Union, but that didn't yet equate to a "civilized" culture relative to the sorts of amenities and conveniences he'd left behind in Kildare. As Matt would learn, joining the Union wasn't especially popular, but it had been a necessity brought on by the government's lack of funds. Matt secured his belongings from the ship and sought out the gentleman – Colonel Kinney – whom he had corresponded with about a house and land. Blessedly, it went easier than one might have supposed, as Matthew Dunn was quickly accommodated. It wouldn't be a palatial estate by any means, but it would do for the present. It would represent the first Dunn family roots in America.

Uncle Matt's brothers and Long Larry had chipped in what they could afford to help him get established in the new land. It would be enough to acquire a quite basic dwelling on a small plot of land. The simple one-room house on a dusty-when-not-muddy, wagon-rutted road overlooked the warm waters of Corpus Christi Bay. As implied, the weather could be quite uncertain. High humidity was fairly constant with Gulf breezes offering little relief. Another downside was the insects; stinging, biting, in-your-face, drive-you-crazy fleas, flies, ants, and similar small but mighty annoyances that proved God could give His bounty on the one hand and extract a price on the other.

Matt's temporary lodging was actually what barely constituted a dwelling, as it consisted of upright poles standing side by side with gaps chinked with sod and moss. The floor consisted of sand and gravel from a nearby creek, and the roof was made of split boards with more of that ever-present, handy sod and moss to stem any leaks. Matt quickly planted a garden in hopes of catching the tail end of the growing season and soon found the local game – mostly deer and wild turkey – could provide a bit of meat. He bartered for sugar and coffee from Mexican traders in Corpus Christi. There wasn't a lot of food variety, but he found creative ways to prepare it. He even bartered for a rooster and three chickens. Matt settled into his simple lodgings, knowing full well that he had to devote full bore to fulfilling his new obligation to serve as sutler to the U.S. Army.

Corpus Christi at that time was a small village of a hundred or so people on the crescent-shaped bay founded after the Spanish explorer Alonzo Álvarez de Pineda sailed into its harbor on the Roman Catholic Feast Day of Corpus Christi in the early 1500s. At least that's one of the accounts as to how the place got its name. The barrier islands between the town and the Gulf of Mexico would become known as the Padre Islands. Corpus Christi's natural harbor had at one time been home to marauding pirates, and its beaches were rumored to hide all manner of buried treasure. Surely, doubloons and reals lurked beneath the sands. It was also the scene of many a raid by local Indians and bandits. Nevertheless, Colonel Henry Lawrence Kinney set up a trading post that would form a hub round which the city would develop and thrive.

Uncle Matt had read as much as possible on the hostilities between the United States and Mexico. He felt that General Taylor's army had a decided advantage, not the least of which was the full support of President James Polk. It was said that President Polk actually had little use for the army except as it might achieve his political ends, including promulgation of a policy called "manifest destiny." This policy expressed the belief that America's providential mission was to expand its reach across all of North America. In short order, it would generate considerable political weight. Originally a partisan issue of the Democratic Party, manifest destiny gained Whig Party adherents as time passed. For this moment in time, however, it was President Polk's mantra. It began with invoking the Texas-Mexico border that was agreed to in the 1836 Treaties of Velasco between the Republic of Texas and Mexico that established the southern-most Texas border as the Rio Grande.

How Matt dealt with his new situation is enlightening, mostly in terms of the cultures blending together in Texas. There was an evolving Irish community in south Texas dating back to the 1820s. It fit neatly into the already heavily Catholic Mexican presence. War with Mexico was imminent, and a new cultural dynamic was being created. With all that in mind, and Matt's concern with building a life in Texas, I imagined him looking out over what seemed like an endless sea of U.S. Army tents set in neat rows as he went to report for duty. Soon enough, it was official. Uncle Matt had signed on to support the United States Army.

The hostilities would begin soon enough. It would be another five months before negotiations between the United States and Mexico to annex New Mexico, Arizona, and California fell apart. Texas was admitted to the Union. Matt took advantage of breaks in his duties to make an occasional wagon ride back into Corpus Christi. He took advantage of this time to build a much-improved clapboard-and-log cabin, splitting wood planks for a solid floor, so he no longer had to slog through any mush and muck after heavy rains. If only he could get rid of the pesky mosquitos. The late-garden crop actually produced some zucchini, a few scraggly beans, some under-sized ears of corn, and some tomatoes. Matt bought a couple of more chickens, and the birds went right to work laying eggs. However, he'd have to continue to barter in the city for flour, salt, and sugar.

Matt later shared how camp life for the soldiers was mostly boring, punctuated only by the monotony of typical tasks like cooking, cleaning latrines, firearms training, and marching drills. As a sutler, he was not a fully enlisted soldier, so he got to bypass most of those duties. When he wasn't in Corpus Christi, he broke up the time by teaching Irish tunes to soldiers in the camp. He remarked how strange the melodies sounded delivered as they were with those "twangy" Texan accents. It seems that the company he supported was comprised mostly of grizzled veterans of the hard-fought Texas War of Independence ten years earlier. Uncle Matt wasn't sure what to expect as concerned his Catholic faith, but it never emerged as a problem. He worked diligently at his sutler duties and was readily accepted into the unit.

Matt told me about serious concerns that Colonel Kinney had with General Taylor's call for volunteers. The signing up of men from around the region had the effect of draining the frontier of fighting men and leaving their families vulnerable. Kinney called for U.S. Government protection. Moreover, the army had stores of provisions that were essentially unguarded due to a shortage of men. Marauding parties were conducting raids of the supply caches. A quote from Kinney's letter to Sam Houston reveals the extent of concern:

> *"The fact of annexation being completed, disarmed our whole population. They literally turned their swords into pruning hooks, and began to forget the calamities and anxieties naturally incident to a border residence, and to cultivate the arts of peace. We are, therefore, without arms or ammunition. We require a small force of regular troops for our protection, and, to do us any good, that assistance should be afforded to us without delay. But in case the government cannot do this, I implore you to endeavor to procure arms and ammunition for such as remains…In haste, as ever, yours truly, H.L. Kinney"*

The outcome of Kinney's letter upon it being referred to the War Department reflected a classic military endorsement. They assured Kinney that General Taylor would "take ample measures for the security of the several towns and settlements." Raids on supplies continued.

I especially recollect Matt's stories of the war itself. I tell them here, as the telling lends itself to more fully understanding the spirit that drove the men who carved out lives on the frontier as exemplified by their willingness to fight for it. Matt tended to get stirred up when he told his story about when the fighting began and his role in it.

In April, with diplomatic negotiations broken down, "Old Rough and Ready's" troops finally broke camp and marched off to a position closer to the Mexican border city of Matamoros, where he established what became known as Fort Texas. Sensing the imminent hostilities, Mexican General Mariano Arista brought a force of about 5,000 men across the Rio Grande upriver from Taylor's Fort Texas location. Arista immediately sent his cavalry into the countryside to harass settlers and the small contingents of U.S. troops that had been sent out for reconnaissance. General Taylor was suspicious of Arista and sent two dragoon companies upriver to investigate. It wasn't long before a Captain Seth Thornton rode his dragoons into an ambush, and his 80-man force was quickly overwhelmed by superior Mexican Army numbers. Reportedly, 11 of his dragoons were killed, and the remainder – including several wounded – were captured. An angry President Polk seized on what was to be called the Thornton Affair to ask Congress to declare war on May 13. They had their pretext.

By now, Matt had been cleared to join the Army as a teamster. His first call to action came one morning in May, as the troops were called to assemble bright and early. It was terribly hot and humid, but at least there was the prospect of action. Excitement reigned throughout the camp. This battle of Palo Alto a bit north of Brownsville would be what was considered the first major engagement of the war.

Matt's tale became quite exciting. With bugles blaring and drums beating out their staccato beat, Matt's company formed up with his wagon full of supplies and joined the rest of Taylor's army in columns of twos and marched off to find the Mexicans. With cannons and chuck wagons in tow, they traveled the 100-mile distance over about eight days to the scrubby, God-forsaken crossroads called Palo Alto. The surrounding land could be best described as miles of rolling sand dunes mostly covered in prairie grass, with a very few scattered live oak mottes. As they crested a rise about 800 yards from General Arista's forces, Matt saw his first Mexican combat troops. From what he told me, I expect his emotions ran a gamut from awe to fear to confidence that all came together in his reliance upon God. He reflexively made the sign of the cross. Even his Protestant fellow soldiers could be heard muttering prayers. Matt said he felt blessed that he was at the rear.

"Fix bayonets! Prime your muskets!" came the commands. A bugle blared out a military flourish. The troops deployed in a two-deep formation about a half-mile long. Most of the troops, Matt included, were equipped with .69 caliber smoothbore flintlocks. With a 100-yard range, they weren't ideal, but they were quite serviceable. The real advantage for the U.S. Army were cannon that fired cannonballs, shells, and canister shot that could be reloaded and fired at five times the rate of the Mexican army's cannon.

General Arista had a slight numerical superiority, but it would be the American cannon that would decide the day. Arista deployed in defensive positions, anticipating Taylor's assault.

As if an arms disadvantage wasn't enough, the Mexican army was not up to the fighting standards of General Taylor's more disciplined, seasoned corps. At the first explosions and whistling of cannonballs and devastation of canister shot, many of the Mexicans began to break ranks and flee.

Even though he was "only" a teamster, Matt did get off one shot, but aimed too high and likely didn't hit anything. Before he knew it, he caught up with his unit that had in turn overrun and engaged the fleeing Mexicans. He later recalled clobbering a Mexican soldier across the side of the head with his rifle butt. The Mexican had run at his wagon, and Matt was simply defending himself. The Mexicans finally had enough and effected a full retreat. General Arista had lost nearly 400 soldiers.

Matt would later show me his uniform from that day and the two places he had to repair from bullet holes. I don't know that he ever revealed that to Sarah, the woman he would marry after the war.

Matt, who by now had been fully assigned teamster duties delivering supplies among the troops, and his comrades in arms followed the retreating Mexicans to a place called Resaca de Palma. Here, General Arista believed he had a terrain advantage that might hold off the Americans' march to relieve a Mexican siege at Fort Texas. General Taylor ordered a surprise full-scale assault on Arista's position led by an artillery barrage featuring deadly canister that decimated counter-attacking Mexican cavalry and troops. Matt's company, part of the 4th U.S. Infantry, surged down the road and overran the Mexican cannon, inflicting severe losses. A withering barrage of cannonballs whistled over Matt's head, covering his unit's charge and quite literally wiping out any Mexicans brave enough to try to hold their ground. The assault quickly caused the Mexican defenses to collapse and Arista's troops to go into another headlong retreat. As Matt shared with me years later, he managed to regain his aim and at least wound a Mexican soldier or two. He told me about several bullets lodged in the wooden sides of his wagon.

Perhaps the toughest part of Matt's experience as he described it came after the battle, as he and other teamsters were called upon to bring their wagons forward to help in clearing the battlefield of dead and wounded, as well as collecting still-serviceable equipment. Aside from the lingering odor from cannon and rifle and the terrible stench of dead soldiers, there were the groans and rasping final breaths of the mortally wounded. Blood flowed across the hard soil. He became intimately familiar with temporary field hospitals and observed horrible surgical methods in less-than-ideal conditions. Seeing stacks of amputated limbs was not unusual. This was the inglorious side of battles that few ever took the time to consider in their glorification of war.

General Taylor's troops plunged onward to Fort Texas, but upon arrival discovered that the Mexicans had already departed to join General Arista's retreat back south below the Rio Grande. Having secured the garrison at Fort Texas, Taylor turned his attention back to the south. It also served as a brief rest for his troops.

After commandeering a sufficient flotilla of boats, Taylor's troops crossed the Rio Grande and quickly overran and occupied Matamoros across from the southernmost tip of Texas. Mexican troops had already mostly vacated Matamoros, as they put up token resistance and headed for the comparative security of Monterrey. Matt would now have the luxury of a short respite from battle, as the ranks of General Taylor's troops swelled with several thousand mostly Texan volunteers. Matt took advantage of his time in Matamoros to learn a bit of Spanish, figuring that it might come in handy one day as he carved out his life in Texas. It didn't take long before he became the Company B unofficial interpreter and trade negotiator. His Spanish with Irish accent was apparently good enough to barter effectively. Coupled with his teamster duties that gave him preferred supply access, Company B ate exceptionally well.

In mid-September, General Taylor made the decision to move against the Mexicans now solidly entrenched in the hill country around Monterrey. With 6,640 men, he finally outnumbered his Mexican opponents. By September 20, the road through Saltillo had been captured, Mexican Commanding General Pedro Ampudia had been cut off from any hope of reinforcement, and his strong fortifications proved no match for an American force, despite the fact that Taylor had left most of his artillery back at Matamoros. As Matt would later share with me, it didn't take long for soldiers to become seasoned veterans used to winning battles. Victory was an elixir of sorts. As I'd learn, it would fit well into the mindset of indomitable courage and will to win that characterized Texans. Long Larry would have been able to relate.

As Matt tells it, he learned that General Taylor's generously humane terms of Mexican surrender at Monterrey earned him the personal ire of President Polk. The president would have apparently been happier with an annihilation of the Mexican forces. President Polk's position could be described as vindictive at best. The punishment for Taylor's humane treatment of the Mexican troops was that about a third of his forces were yanked from under his command by President Polk and sent south to support General Winfield Scott's march on Mexico City.

Matt sensed that he should feel fortunate to have remained with Taylor's now somewhat less-experienced 4,600-man occupying force at Saltillo. However, there would be no rest for U.S. troops. War is an uncertain undertaking, after all. It did not take long for General Antonio Lopez de Santa Anna to recognize the American troop reduction as a military opportunity. He'd been officially reelected "president" of Mexico and sought an opportunity to solidify his power by routing a supposed weaker foe.

But the bivouac in Monterrey turned out to be not so easy for Matt, as he was very fortunate to survive an ambush of one of the supply trains he was part of. A roving company of mounted Mexican lancers set and sprung a trap along the Saltillo Road that Matt's supply train frequented. As Matt described it, wagons were burned and the bodies of those killed were mutilated. Matt, along with a man named John Pritchett, was lucky to escape by finding a nearby gulley with plenty of natural cover. All the other drivers and the guards were either killed or captured. Matt and Pritchett were able to make their escape once the Mexican lancers had departed. Some of the captives were tortured to gain information about U.S. troop locations, so it was great fortune that Uncle Matt escaped.

Following the Saltillo massacre, Matt took on duties as a courier and dispatch bearer. I think it was a welcome relief for him after experiencing the tactical vulnerability of the teamsters with their ponderously slow and exposed wagons. I would have similar experiences years later guarding my father's wagon trains full of cotton headed for Mexico during the War Between the States.

Matt told how he was amazed at how the Mexicans fought back despite being at a military disadvantage. Santa Anna now chose to move north from Mexico City with a 20,000-man army and plans to crush the Americans once and for all. Learning of the Mexican strategy, Taylor dug in at Hacienda de Buena Vista, where he controlled a strategically located mountain pass. By the time Santa Anna reached Buena Vista, desertions had reduced his Mexican force to around 15,000 very tired troops. Nevertheless, Santa Anna wasted no time taking advantage of his numerical superiority and ordering an all-out assault of Taylor's position on September 23. His attack stalled. Despite what would later be judged an unwise, even audacious counterattack, Taylor commanded his troops to charge headlong into Santa Anna's troops, totally confusing the Mexicans' plans. By dark, more than 3,400 Mexicans lay dead or wounded versus Taylor's loss of around 650 troops. Soundly trounced, General Santa Anna declared victory and limped away. He had pretty much had enough of these American soldiers, especially those from Texas. With his reputedly extra-large ego, he couldn't accommodate the embarrassment of losing once again to the Texans. His embarrassing loss to Sam Houston at San Jacinto back in 1836 in the Texas War for Independence apparently was wedged deeply in his craw.

Finally, with General Scott's victory at Mexico City, the war was brought to an end, and the order came to withdraw back to Texas. Matt read to his troop mates the news report of the signing of the Treaty of Guadalupe Hidalgo on February 2, 1848. The treaty granted the United States the Rio Grande boundary and what would become New Mexico, California, Nevada, Utah, and sections of Arizona, Wyoming, and Colorado. As he read, Matt first became aware of how humiliating it must have been for Mexico to be unable to defend its territory. Despite the United States paying Mexico $15 million and granting U.S. citizenship to any Mexicans who chose to remain in those newly annexed territories, the war would have a long-lived psychological impact upon those who fought it and for the generations that followed.

It would leave an indelible imprint on the psyche that is Texas. By Matt's telling, it certainly had an impact on me.

Matt returned to Corpus Christi. With no anticipation of engaging in further battle, it made for a long march home. He began to think on settling down. In the course of settling in ahead of actually reporting for his earlier sutler duties, Matt happened to have met a lovely lass named Sarah Pritchett. After the war, they courted and married. I recall the joy that Matt expressed in his letter to Long Larry. He even had Sarah pen a note for his mother (my grandmother). Uncle Matt felt confident that his letter would be shared with the entire family. He'd found his future. He'd become a Texan.

Sarah held onto the belief that the man who had escaped the Saltillo Massacre with Uncle Matt was her brother John Pritchett, but they lost track and were never to see him again. The war was over. Now, they could begin their life in America in earnest. It wasn't long before they discovered Sarah was pregnant. Family was the glue to settling the frontier, as children furnished the roots essential to a flourishing Texas.

Uncle Matt had also continued to develop a friendship with Colonel Henry Lawrence Kinney, who had deeded 100 acres of land to him out of gratitude for his services. Keep in mind that, as one of the founders of Corpus Christi, the colonel had great influence on the development of the region. The land he gave to Matt was located on the old San Patricio Road (now Up River Road) about five miles west of Corpus Christi. At the time, the population was so thin that there was apparently only one house standing between Uncle Matt's place and Corpus Christi proper. After building a house on this property, Matt began to work out a living by tilling the soil. He used his muster-out pay to purchase seed and additional implements to plant enough garden to feed his family and then some. On occasional journeys into Corpus Christi, he began to inquire about ranching. With vast land resources available, he saw the potential for raising cattle and possibly some horses. It turned out that the plentiful cattle and wild horses were descended from stock cultivated decades earlier by Spanish Conquistadors. His only previous livestock experience had been with a few sheep back in Kildare, but he was intent on learning ranching. He went to Gonzales and bought a few head of cattle from a Mr. Zumolt. Matt adopted Mr. Zumolt's "Z" brand as his own.

He and Sarah apparently lived a good life despite Matt missing the family back in Ireland. Colonel Kinney frequently stopped by, and they would often pass the time on Sundays at afternoon cock fights. In fact, Matt kept the colonel's cocks for him, making sure they were in fighting trim.

As uncivilized as the practice may seem to many folks, cock fighting was pretty much a part of life in South Texas. Cock fighting had been around for roughly 6,000 years, as I hear tell. I do confess that, at the tender age of sixteen, I witnessed a couple of these contests. Colonel Kinney's cocks apparently had a reputation as being among the most vicious. It took a couple of years of preparing these cocks for the fights. In the fights I witnessed, they had spurs attached to their talons that made them even more formidable. People would come from miles around to see and bet on the fights. It was hot and raucous as patrons rooted for their favorites. Notably, the fights ended with one or both cocks in any given contest bloodied and often killed. Most of Colonel Kinney's fighting cocks fought very well. The people attending the fights were at times nastier than the fighting cocks, as wagering could get heavy. The crowd consisted of Texans and Mexicans, so there was bad blood to begin with. Colonel Kinney did his utmost to keep the crowd civil, and Uncle Matt helped maintain order. More than once, he had to separate human combatants.

It's important to the Dunn story to keep in mind that Kinney was passionate about developing Corpus Christi as a thriving port and regularly encouraged Matt to get his brothers to join him in Texas. Matt forwarded a copy of an advertisement Colonel Kinney had placed in a small newssheet called "The Nueces Valley," published out of Corpus Christi. It read as follows:

ONE HUNDRED FAMILIES WANTED

To any family that will settle on my land twelve miles from Corpus Christi, on the Nueces River, I will let them have Ten Cows on shares for ten years; will sell them One Hundred Acres of land adjoining; for One Dollar an Acre; one yoke of Oxen, and one Horse – all to be paid for at the end of Ten Years, with interest annually.

The soil and climate are unsurpassed, water abundant, and a market for all that can be raised. There are three companies of Rangers in the vicinity to protect the frontier, and Government is determined to establish permanent posts, so there may be no apprehension of future trouble with the Indians.

I will also give One Town Lot to each family, on the town plat that is to be laid off.

You may ask, why this liberality? I have thirty odd square leagues of land here in solid body, and 10,000 Cattle. I want the land improved and its resources developed now.

Each family should be furnished with the necessary farming implements and provisions for one year. For further particulars, apply to the subscriber.

H.L. Kinney

I learned that Kinney ran the ad again on July 13, 1850 with an accompanying list of animals that Indians had stolen from the Colonel. I expect that spoke volumes about the security of the Texas frontier, but the Dunn family wasn't dissuaded.

Importantly, and per Colonel Kinney's urgings, Uncle Matt wrote again to Long Larry and to his brothers, this time inviting them to join him in this incredible American adventure. Matt knew it could be months before Long Larry would receive his letter back in Kildare. He painted a picture of an almost biblical "land of milk and honey" and assured him that he was healthy and beginning to make a life in America. He took care not to mention the voracious fleas and mosquitos or the predatory Indians.

Of course, I got to see Uncle Matt's letter to my father. From that point forward, all I could think about was going to Texas.

There apparently were tales of Comanche sightings, but not much confirmation. That being said, Uncle Matt did hear about a couple of fights with Indians near the city. Around Corpus Christi, it was more likely that folks would encounter Mexican raiders or banditos that would venture north of the Rio Grande. There was a sort of undeclared warfare between Mexicans and Texans that would linger long after the war. Still, Matt, Sarah, and the boys had to hide a couple of times from marauding Comanche and Lipan Apache. It was unnerving to say the least, and I would later come to fully appreciate their fears.

Uncle Matt's letter was full of promise for a new life, but it would be later – after my father and I had immigrated to Texas – that he would share with us some of his feelings from the battlefield – the cries of the wounded and the stench of death. I'd recall him mentioning manifest destiny and the politics of free versus slave states, but even he was vague about these issues as rationales shaping the nation. Still, he felt like he'd become a true American and a truer Texan by virtue of fighting for his newly adopted country.

Unfortunately, ranching and farming wouldn't last for long for Uncle Matt. After John B. (a.k.a., Red John) was born, he and Sarah had a second son Matthew and, soon after, she became pregnant with their third son James. However, Uncle Matt suffered a severe sunstroke while working in his fields. Likely as not, it was a very hot day, and he had not drunk enough water nor protected himself adequately from the sun's blast. The sunstroke apparently affected his mind such that he was never the same. Since there was no asylum or appropriate hospital available in Texas to care for him, Uncle Matt was sent to New Orleans, Louisiana for treatment. As we were later told, he was transferred around 1863 to another hospital in Baton Rouge.

Rumor had it that he drowned accidentally during transport. We can never be certain, but I do know that family support payments from the army stopped. Fortunately, I would arrive in Texas before Uncle Matt's sunstroke so was blessed with having spent time with him and listened to his stories first hand.

Matt's wife, Sarah, continued to live on the farm and operate it. Keep in mind that she had three young children at the time: "Red John," aged four; Matt, aged two; and Jim, not quite aged one. Sarah was widely known in the region as "Aunt Sarah" and was a very hospitable, happy person whom all the relatives loved to visit.

But I'm just a tad ahead of my story, as I haven't yet shared how I came to immigrate to Texas. The saga of the Dunn family in south Texas had, however, taken solid root. A new story – mine – began to take shape. A Texas dynasty – a destiny – had been born.

THREE

Irishman in the Nueces River Valley

Y'all can go to hell. I'm going to Texas.

Davey Crockett

You'd likely be justified in asking what might lead a lad of only fifteen years of age to leave his homeland and trade his kilt for trousers on a vast and God-awful rough frontier. The heathers and forests of Kildare are beautiful, but...well...there are times in our lives when reason must trump emotion.

I've described how the potato famine and persecutions by the British had driven Uncle Matt to leave Ireland. It would get worse. There was a terrible famine in Ireland during the years 1847 to 1848. Thousands of impoverished Irish died of starvation. It was not uncommon to see whole families escaping to the cities. Of course, the cities weren't equipped to handle the onslaught of refugees. The resulting environment fostered disease and pestilence. On more than one occasion I had to pass dead bodies by the roadside, honest folk who starved to death. People did what they could to get by – men went to workhouses, women fell into prostitution, families stood in lines at the soup kitchens that began to spring up, and many dug through trash heaps for a measly subsistence. Far too many gave up. As I understand it, the farther west one headed in our country, the worse the conditions.

Landlords were quick to evict tenants who failed to pay rent. All in all, life had become quite desperate.

As if to magnify the horror, the English continued to ship to England most of the healthy crops that were produced in Ireland, especially oats and barley. Coupled with the continued ill treatment inflicted by the Lord Overseers upon the Irish people, it was far too much to bear for most folk. The English saw their Irish subjects as mere barbarians, an order barely more civilized than mindless animals. The religious strife of Irish Catholic versus the Protestant Church of England made things all the worse. The only salvation beyond the Irish peoples' strong faith was the strength of the heritage passed on by their ancestors. The legends, the tales, the songs, the culture would never be – could never be – defeated by the English.

As for me, I was experiencing the tensions first hand. I regularly ran afoul of the Lord Overseer's children. Lord Overseers had been the result of a codification of Statutes at Large as enacted by Parliaments held in Ireland. Despite my youth, I understood clearly the shameless ruse perpetrated by the Statutes' codes. It seemed as though these overseers could steal and bully with impunity. I was not one to truck with being bullied, and I'm sure my father worried that at some time I'd go too far in defending myself. I tried to tread along a fine line without going too far. As a Catholic, I was a target. Keep in mind that there was the matter of the Church of England, established back in 1836, stemming from King Henry VIII's resistance to the Pope in Rome. I expect my attitude didn't help, but what else could be expected from a descendant of Long Larry Dunn? My grandfather's blood ran strong in my veins. I heard more than one tale of him defending our family honor or standing by a friend in a brawl. I remember Long Larry as a big man and strong as an ox. While kind-hearted, he was not to be trifled with.

Late one afternoon, as my younger brother Lawrence and I headed home from work in the fields, two of the Lord Overseer's sons blocked my path. As I recall, the encounter went as follows.

"Hey, Paddy! Where do you think you're going?' The taller of the boys threw out a challenge. I think his name was Edmund, though that likely doesn't matter. He was just another British thug so far as I was concerned – just younger than most. He undoubtedly felt his father's position granted him some sort of extended entitlement. Paddy? That was a derogatory name the British tossed around.

I stopped but said nothing. I half-glanced at my brother. Even though he was two years younger than me, I was emboldened by his presence. I wasn't about to let my little brother down. I even had the temerity to make eye contact with this Edmund character.

The shorter of the two – I think his name was John – drew closer and pushed his finger hard into my shoulder. "Can you talk, Paddy?"

I didn't want trouble, but I could see this becoming physical. I recalled my grandfather's and my father's advice to avoid a fight but never back down.

"You Cat-liks are cowards. Can't none of you fight?" He moved his finger to my chest and pressed harder. He turned his head toward his companion. "Lookee, see what cowards these Cat-lik Paddys be?" Of course, he knew we could fight but figured we wouldn't want to bring down the wrath of his father, the Lord Overseer, on our heads.

The nickname was not so bad, but insulting my faith cut to my core. If they wanted trouble, they had picked the wrong Irishman. Edmund's nose – a long hooked protuberance reddened by the cold air – was a worthy target, but his companion was nearer at hand.

I brought my knee up into the groin of the shorter boy, and he doubled over in pain. Edmund took a wild swing at me. "Damn you, Paddy!" He missed, and I landed my own fist square on the tip of that long nose. I could hear it crack and drew back as blood spattered down his tunic.

I left the two of them groveling with pain on the road and headed home. Lawrence trotted along beside me. "Whoa, Nick…you sure can deliver a punch!" I appreciated his admiration but feared the consequences of what I'd done.

I recall the fearful expression on my father's face as he confronted me after hearing about my encounter. "My dear son, your Uncles Peter and Thomas are getting ready to join Matt in that Texas place. Methinks it's time for you to realize your dreams of travel and adventure. Indeed, it's time." It was wise counsel. The Lord Overseer's boys would surely seek retribution, and it might not be pretty.

Matt's glowing account of the land of promise in the new state of Texas had finally inspired two of his brothers to follow him: Peter in 1850 and Thomas about the same time. It was a brave, bold act to leave our homeland. I was fifteen at the time and would accompany my Uncle Peter. My father wasn't quite ready to set sail for America but, coupled with the aftermath of the potato famine plus his fear of more of my seemingly unavoidable and ever-more-frequent encounters with the British, he sensed the strong spirit of adventure in me and let me go. Besides, my grandfather Long Larry had filled my head with all manner of tales real or imagined about Texas. He likely exaggerated just a bit, but images of vast prairies, endless skies, rich soil, and plentiful wildlife fed my all-too-vivid imagination. On the other hand, my Uncle Patrick was intent on sticking it out in Kildare...more on that later. In part, I think it was mostly because my grandfather was getting on in years. Long Larry was strong but, at age seventy-five, was beginning to struggle with his health. I do think he felt blessed that his sons were pursuing opportunities that would likely never materialize in Kildare or other parts of Ireland, for that matter.

I admit that it was especially tough to leave Mother and my brothers, but Texas and the high adventure it conjured up in my young fertile imagination was calling me. The fight with the Lord Overseer's boys was only part of my motivation. My grandfather Long Larry, my father, and my mother, along with my brothers and sisters, gathered on the dock to see me and my uncles off. There were plenty of hugs and prayers for a safe voyage. I struggled to hold back a tear or two as I hugged Mother.

Long Larry sidled up to me. He pressed a small Celtic cross into my hand. "Nicholas Dunn, I am and will ever be proud of you. Remember all you've been taught, apply it, and you will do well. If you do right things, right things will happen, my boy. Be ready to seize opportunities and always do well with them." These words would become prophetic as I built my life in Texas.

With Matt already in Texas, we'd become ever more appreciative of our family. The family spirit was strong in Ireland as it was, what with clans and sects, but there was naught like family members departing and perhaps never to be seen again to forge closer bonds of love for those left behind. Now, three more of Long Larry's family were departing. It was a hauntingly sad, yet uplifting time.

Soon enough, the salt sea air filled my lungs and my thoughts turned to the excitement of adventures that surely lay ahead. Our stout little ship was buffeted twice by storms, but we endured the nearly three-month voyage. Honestly, I only got sick once, and that was an especially rough day. The howling wind against the wave-battered ship gave an eerie wail not unlike an Irish banshee's *caoine* or dirge from somewhere in the depths of the roiling sea. We passed the time singing songs, telling tales from the homeland, and looking out for the sea monsters that surely lurked in the ocean's depths. We tried to spend as much time as possible on deck, as the ship hold where we slept was dank, slick from rain and seawater, and unimaginably cramped. We likely as not brought fewer belongings than did my Uncle Matt, but that was more by necessity than desire. My father did send his plow ahead with me in anticipation of his soon leaving Ireland with the rest of my family. Of course, my Uncle Peter brought his smithy tools. We'd have what we needed to begin to establish our lives in Texas.

At least the final month of the voyage was graced with warmer climes and ever more crystalline blue waters. We first landed in New Orleans, where we spent time getting our land legs and our bearings in this new land. It was a crowded, busy place full of color and what they called a Cajun French heritage. It evoked promise of a grand new adventure, and it wasn't but a very few days later that we boarded a boat to Corpus Christi – and our future.

When we arrived in Corpus Christi, Uncle Matt, Sarah, and their newborn son John were at the dock to greet us. There were tears of relief, plenty of laughter, and great hugs. And, it was wonderful to be standing once again on something that wasn't swaying with the waves. We were with family again. Most important, I felt an overwhelming sense of freedom. Yes, there was fear, but it was more than offset by this journey of adventure I was fulfilling. I had reached the destination of my dreams. I was ready to explore this great unknown land called Texas. In a way, I felt I was fulfilling my grandfather's unrealized dreams of adventure. I sensed Long Larry's spirit near at hand, as though I was living his dreams vicariously.

We were quickly introduced to that dreamed-about "land of milk and honey." What we found was rough open country – mostly prairie – with a few scattered mottes of what I learned were live oak and some parts covered with dense brush, occasional mesquite trees, ebony, cat claw, chaparral, live oak, and other native trees and brush. Many were evergreen. Now and then, balls of brush called tumbleweeds rolled by. Most of the plants bore thorns and beautiful flowers but no edible fruit. Along the river banks grew pecan trees and wild grapes. Some fields of bluebonnets had just flowered, and they were an amazing sight to behold. The grass grew so high that it would just about tickle a horse's belly. There was a lot of cactus, covered with yellow and pink flowers, which bore a small fruit. The succulent fruit was covered with thorns and was full of seeds. I learned that children sometimes ate them, and the increasingly friendly Mexicans prepared a tasty dish of the tender young leaves. It was reassuring to know that I wouldn't starve. Pecan trees were plentiful along the nearby Nueces River, and I quickly learned that *nueces* was a Spanish word for nuts.

My Uncle Matt told me that the name Texas – as he learned from

Colonel Kinney – was used by the Spanish explorers to describe an area peopled by the Hasinai branch of the Caddoan Indians called Teychas. Teychas meant ally or friend. The Spaniards corrupted it as Tejas and, more frequently, as Texas. At least this is how I understood the origin of the name to have come about.

Texas was a mostly dry, semi-tropical country and apparently suffered from protracted droughts. Despite the droughts, the air remained quite humid, thanks to Corpus Christi Bay and the Gulf of Mexico. I learned that the normal annual rainfall was a paltry 27 inches or so. When it did rain, mosquitos and mud abounded. The land was not fenced in, so there was free range for livestock. I'll share later how that was a blessing and a curse. The rich soil produced good crops when there was sufficient rainfall, but there was very little land in cultivation. Wild cattle – mostly longhorns – and mustang horses roamed the prairies. Given the sparse vegetation, the cattle were pretty much spread far and wide to find adequate forage. Wild pigs, turkeys, coyotes, squirrels, deer, fox, quail, javelina, wolves, panthers, and other native animals were also plentiful. I was told that some buffalo could be found if you cared to venture northwest into Comanche territory.

My Uncle Peter – with whom I had sailed across the Atlantic – didn't waste any time establishing his much-needed smithy trade in Corpus Christi. He built his blacksmith shop on Water Street and, on the door, he started a tradition of heating each iron until it was red hot and then burning in every brand he ever crafted. The smithy business – and ranching – thrived, as eventually attested to by the many brands burned into his door, the regular turnover of horses in his stable as they awaited shoeing, and the numerous tools he fashioned and hung for sale near the entrance to his shop.

Since Uncle Matt's home with Sarah and the children was a bit cramped, I made do with reasonable comfort in a room atop Uncle Peter's blacksmith shop.

I joined in to alternately help Uncle Peter with his smithy work, and Uncles Matt and Thomas with raising livestock and a wee bit of farming. I recognized that it would be helpful to learn a bit of the smithy trade as well as farming and ranching. I wouldn't have long to wait before my own family would be coming to America. Meanwhile, I must admit to eating quite well, especially at Uncle Matt's house. I did long for my Mother's great cooking. I tried to learn as much as I could about Texas and its people. At Uncle Matt's urging, I began to learn a bit of Spanish. Like Matt, it was colored with my own Irish brogue. Imagine, if you will, what eventually happened as it took on what the native Texans called a southern twang. It was a sing-song sound, rather light and airy like the traditional Celtic tongue of Ireland. I think the uniqueness of the Texas twang helped in establishing what made Texas a special place.

Uncle Matt would regale me with stories he'd heard of Texas independence, of the time before statehood. I learned about the sad but inspiring tragedies of the Alamo and Goliad, as well as the exploits of Stephen F. Austin and Sam Houston and the great victory at San Jacinto that marked the true beginnings of the Republic of Texas and ultimately enabled statehood in 1845.

Later in 1851, my dear father, John, finally brought our family to Texas. Now, four of Long Larry Dunn's five sons had immigrated to America. My brother John and my sister Annie would both be born in Texas.

I recall how incredibly grand it was to greet my mother on the dock. By this time, I fancied myself an official Texan, having even captured a touch of that Texas twangy drawl combined with a hint of Irish brogue. Naturally, the entire family immersed in hugs and those sorts of carryings on, but it was my mother that I had missed the most. I wasn't ready to admit that, of course, as the guys greeted each other with the usual man hugs. But there's nothing like the bond with your mother. And I must say that my mother was the prototypical Dunn mother. She was beautiful, loving, tough, sensible, compassionate, resourceful, and fiercely loyal.

My father was decked out in his kilt for the occasion of their arrival, but I don't recall seeing him ever wear it again save for family weddings. The kilt was simply not appropriate to the rough flora and fauna of South Texas. That having been said, he cut a fine figure in that kilt as he stepped onto the dock.

With the family reunited, the seemingly unlimited promise of this new land lay before us. Unlike the northeastern cities and states where immigrants often found themselves isolated in crowded ghettos of their own nationality, Texas welcomed everyone inclusively – Irish, German, Dutch, or whomever – with open arms. We were now Texans – Irish by birth, certainly – but Texans foremost. We hadn't yet fully realized it, but we were the beginnings of a western push of settlement that would conquer the frontier.

Land was very cheap: five dollars an acre near town, ranging downward from that price to five cents per acre 50 miles from town. We seriously considered Colonel Kinney's aforementioned offer, but went our own way. My father soon acquired some Nueces County land from a gentleman named Jonas Pickles about five miles west of town between the Nueces Bay and what would later become the Texas Mexican Railroad right-of-way. We quickly erected a simple clapboard house that provided immediate shelter and would later be a storage building. My father built with his own hands the house we lived in – and we grew up in – until his death nearly forty years later. It was a well-built house, though not a large one, and was located roughly half a mile from and overlooking the Nueces Bay. Many years later, part of the land would become the site of St. Theresa's Church and school, with the house serving as the parish house.

I vividly recall playing with my brothers and my sister Annie. There seemed no end of opportunities to find trouble masked as fun. We quickly learned to avoid those ugly, foul-smelling, wild pigs and plentiful but nasty turkeys, not to mention snakes. My, but my dear sister Annie was scared to death of snakes. When we killed an occasional rattlesnake, we'd always be sure to show the rattler's corpse to poor Annie. As second oldest after my brother Christopher and having already accommodated life in the new land, I usually led any shenanigans that went on. You might say I was the de facto leader of the Dunn children. Naturally, I maintained my hold over my sister and younger brothers by telling stories of frontier horrors, embellishing tales of attacks by javelina or the tortures inflicted on captives by Comanche.

But, back to the home my father built. There were several smaller buildings detached from the main building of the house. One was the dining room and kitchen. Since it didn't rain all that much, having detached buildings was no big thing. Later, my father expanded the main house and "repurposed" the outbuildings. There was also a large circular underground cistern, made of material composed of sand and shell from the shores of the Nueces Bay. Beneath the house, there was a basement or cellar – as it was called in those days – something that very few houses in this part of the country had at the time owing to the hard, dry nature of the soil. It helped keep the air circulating in the house during stretches of hot weather, and it was thought to afford protection from any threats like Comanche, Apache, or those ever-present desperadoes.

The two front rooms of the main house were large. My memory serves to give me a clear picture of the parlor. It was two steps lower than the master's bedroom. The parlor featured horse-hair upholstered furniture, marble top tables, rich mahogany finishes, and ornately framed pictures of the famed Irish heroes Daniel O'Connell and Robert Emmet, as well as a large painting of all the popes from Pope Peter to Pope Leo XIII.

As a serious and religious-minded pioneer, my father gathered quite an impressive library for his time. His library included *The Holy Bible*, three volumes of *Lives of the Saints*, *Lives of Irish Saints and Martyrs*, Geoffrey Keating's *History of Ireland*, Clareten's *History of Ireland*, a *History of the Christian Church*, lectures and sermons by Father Burke titled *Instructions for Youth*, Hume's *History of England*, *Trials of a Mind*, Moore's *Life of Lord Edward Fitzgerald*, *Washington and His Generals*, a *Bible History*, and Cobbet's *History of the Reformation*. Clearly, he was Long Larry Dunn's son. He made certain that we all availed ourselves of the knowledge bursting from the pages of those books.

Most rooms had fireplaces, though the kitchen fireplace was relatively large and used more for cooking than warmth. Of course, the weather was mostly too hot to worry much about stoking fires for warmth in the bedrooms. I recall that my father hung two muskets over the fireplace mantle. They were ready to shoot should the occasion arise. We did have to run and hide from Comanche threats a couple of times.

A large four-poster bed with canopy over it dominated my folk's bedroom. In one corner, there was a large wardrobe of mahogany, a sofa to match, and a center table with rocking chairs. The rest of the house consisted of a couple of smaller bedrooms and a large one in the attic, an entry hall between my parent's room and the pantry, and a long front porch across the front – the gallery, as we called it.

Of course, there was the outhouse – a two-holer! This was the height of convenience in these parts. Indoor plumbing simply wasn't available or even known. Roughly every three or four months, we'd dig new holes and move the contraption. I won't pursue this any further other than to say toilet paper wasn't invented until 1857 and was scarce for years after that. Well, actually, we used dry corn cobs kept in a handy box outside the outhouse. Okay, not really, but it makes for a good yarn.

The large yard was enclosed with a white picket fence. There was a long grape arbor, a number of plum trees, a peach tree, several shade trees and flowers, a vegetable garden, barn, stables, stock pens, sheds, chicken house, pig pen, and a good well. Despite the threats of Comanche, Apache, and bandits, there was a sense of safety in this place. It was like heaven on Earth compared to what we'd left behind in Ireland. The rolling hills of Ireland were never forgotten, mind you, but quickly became only fond memories. Texas had indeed become our land of milk and honey.

From time to time, my father would gather me and my brothers to hunt or fish. We had a lot of success, as game was plentiful. Wild pigs – javelina – were especially challenging, as they could be nasty critters, stunk to high heaven, and were downright vicious when cornered. Deer, ducks, and quail were easier fare…tasty, too. This hunting time served to keep life in balance, as it was far too easy to get totally immersed in my fledgling business endeavors. It's notable, too, that the prairies and scrub of the Nueces Strip featured millions of head of scrawny Mexican longhorn cattle roaming wild with no fences to contain them. There were also large bunches of mustang horses, plenty of deer, and buffalo in herds of thousands or more.

It was around this time that I had the great fortune to acquire a .44 caliber 1847 Walker Colt revolver. The contraption was about fifteen inches long and weighed in at nearly five pounds. It wasn't worth a hoot for hunting but would be handy against Comanche or desperadoes. I also learned that the cylinder on the Walker Colt tended to rupture at inopportune times, as they hadn't quite worked out the metallurgy to withstand heavy charges. I much preferred my old percussion caplock plains rifle as my weapon of choice for hunting. It was reliable, accurate, and plenty adequate for most of the game we hunted.

We had to learn a bit of self-sufficiency out on the Texas frontier, and hunting offered a great opportunity to supplement our diet. I recall one hunt that was mostly typical of these ventures. One day in the late summer, my father called me and my brothers together for a hunt. He had announced at dinner the night before that we'd gather early. We had high hopes of bagging some deer and enjoying venison for the week ahead. We were always cautious in venturing out, as you could never be certain whether an Apache or Comanche war party might be lurking about. On this day, my brothers Joseph, Michael, Patrick, and Christopher remained home to work and keep a lookout for any hostiles that might turn up. That left John II, Lawrence, Matthew, and me to join my father. We brought along a burro to transport our bounty home. We were each armed with a newly-acquired Sharps carbine and a Bowie knife, the blade made famous by Alamo defender Jim Bowie, though a lot more refined than his. I also had my Colt Walker revolver stuck in my waistband. I had to cinch my belt extra tight to keep my pants up given the added weight. Mother had packed us some victuals, so we marched off with great confidence if not creature comfort. We hiked roughly five miles to the west, being ever-vigilant for varmints. Wild longhorns could be especially dangerous, not to mention those nasty javelina. Once we reached an area that my father thought seemed about right, he asked John II and me to stay with the burro while they fanned out. We tied the burro to a nearby live oak and sat down to await the gunshots that would surely indicate a kill. After all, what chance did a deer have against three formidable hunters? Keep in mind that the grassy prairie extended for hundreds of miles, broken only by scattered mottes or clumps of usually live oak or mesquite. The scrawny Mexican longhorn cattle roamed wild over this vast unfenced area, and there were also large bunches of mustang horses and sometimes deer and buffalo in herds of a thousand or more.

John whispered, "Nick, how long do you think it will take?"

I shrugged. On previous hunts, we might bag a deer or two inside of a quarter hour. Game was that plentiful. "I don't think we'll have time to eat before we hear the first shot." I laughed quietly. Our hunters were downwind, and noise from us could be a distraction.

About this time, we heard a rustling in some high grass on the other side of a motte of live oak perhaps a hundred feet away. It was the wrong direction to be from my father or brothers.

"Nick," hissed John through tight lips, "could it be Comanche?"

We reflexively brought our rifles into position pointing in the direction of the sound. The sound stopped, then started again just a bit louder and nearer. In rapid succession, the burro snorted, a shot rang out, we heard Lawrence shout "I got him," and three javelina came charging out of the brush at John and me.

The stopping power of a Sharps carbine was legendary, but they were single-shot, breech-loading rifles. They weren't intended for close range. We stopped two of the wild pigs with well-placed shots, but the third was headed straight at John. The Colt found its way into my hand, and I fired as fast as the Colt would allow. I emptied the gun before the javelina stopped about four feet from my brother.

John looked down at the javelina and then at me, "Thank God you can shoot, brother." We were half-crying and half-laughing out of relief at about the time my father and brothers burst onto the scene. They were relieved to say the least.

The javelina did stink to high heaven. It was no wonder that a wound from the tusks of one of these beasts could cause a nasty – even deadly – infection. Lawrence and Matthew went back and dragged the buck from where it had been shot. We field-dressed our prizes. We covered our noses to dress out those stinking wild pigs. All the while, we talked animatedly on how close John had come to being gored by the javelina. My father reminded us that it had been a wise decision to purchase those Sharps carbines but how handy the Colt revolver had been. Slow-cooked and well-seasoned, we knew that the javelina meat would be a delicious alternative to venison or other game.

My mother was pleased at our plentiful bounty. While we'd soften our hunting tale for her ears, we'd regale our younger brothers with a slightly embellished version. It got even better with my uncles.

Our home became widely known for its hospitality, with many persons visiting and enjoying our friendly Irish spirit. Even Catholic Mass would often be held in our home.

I'd later find one of my father's old account books that gives insight as to day-to-day life here in Texas. He journeyed to Corpus Christi pretty much weekly to purchase supplies that included foodstuffs and household necessities like cloves, cinnamon, sugar, crackers, shoes, straw hats, drinking glasses, candles, woolen socks, nails, and rope. Another typical entry I found amusing at the time was for "2 bottles best whiskey." The whiskey cost $1.50, a lot of money at the time.

We often made our own brand of fun. One day, I told a tale of a ghost near our property that came out at night. My father insisted there was no such thing. To prove it, he went out to the wood pile one evening and gathered an armful of logs. Just as he reached the top step of the gallery, a big white object jumped out at him from behind the house hollering "Oooooo!" He threw the armful of wood on the creature's head. That hurt. I was the ghost. I vowed never to play ghost again.

We had a growing immigrant Irish population west of Corpus Christi. We didn't realize how strange our accents sounded to the community, not to mention our Irish lore and customs. Children we'd encounter in Corpus Christi used to urge us to talk just so they could hear our Irish accents. It was meant in good-natured fun.

My father began acquiring large amounts of property in Nueces County, and he put it to practical use raising sheep and growing cotton. He'd had the presence of mind to send that plow with me on my voyage, so was ready to cultivate the land from the moment our homestead had been established. We raised what was called Sea Island cotton. Father would also become known for his philanthropic land donations to the Catholic Church. Indeed, this was a promised land come quite real for the Dunn family. We were becoming Texans. I penned a letter to my grandfather, Long Larry, telling him about the adventurous encounter with javelina on our deer hunt. He'd understand, as the javelina would have been equivalent to the wild boars found in Irish forests. Of course, I exaggerated our bravery in the face of danger. As was my habit when writing to him, I invited him to join us. I knew it wouldn't happen. He was getting on in years. I prayed that my letters reassured him that he'd been right in encouraging our immigration to Texas.

Christmas in our new land presented an opportunity to stay strongly connected with our Irish heritage. My mother would put a candle in each window, a symbol of welcome to travelers – traditionally Mary and Joseph. A wreath of holly was affixed to our front door. My father would awaken us on Christmas Day with the traditional Gaelic greeting *Nollaig Shona Duit* (null-ig hun-a dit), which meant Happy Christmas.

It wasn't long before my father acquired 4,000 acres of land on Petronila Creek southwest of Corpus Christi. Petronila Creek was named after a Spanish land grant to José Antonio Cabazos many years ago. We put 200 acres into cultivation and the rest into grazing land for livestock. My father seized the opportunities to experiment with different crops as afforded by the rich Texas soil. My brother John helped work my father's holdings, and we would eventually acquire roughly 12,000 acres of ranchland. I recall his advice to never sell a heifer calf, as the resulting careful herd management would lead to a steady increase in the size of our herd. We owned the first cotton gin in the region. Of course, we grew and traded cotton. Cotton was labor-intensive agriculture and demanded plenty of workers. My father hired family members to work the fields, but one of the more colorful characters he employed was a Belgian man named August Vandavell, who had been a soldier in Maximillian's army in Mexico. With limited paid-labor availability, my father did own "a few slaves."

Eli Whitney's invention was a godsend for the cotton growers. My father also acquired a hand-operated machine for baling the cotton. While I can't say in retrospect that I'm proud of it, our operations were becoming part-plantation and part-ranch. There were day-to-day dangers on a working ranch. My father endured one incident whereby he was injured by a longhorn bull. The beast hooked him in the mouth, knocking out several teeth and tearing open his cheek. It healed up fine, but left him with an uneven smile.

Father endeavored to give my brothers the best education that he could. Matt, Joe, Mike, and John attended Father Gonnard's school in Corpus Christi, taught by Mr. William Carroll. As each of my brothers completed his studies in this school, Father took them to St. Mary's College in San Antonio, Texas, where each would study for about another two years. My sister Annie would eventually attend the Ursuline Convent in San Antonio. Unfortunately, Lawrence and I were older and missed out on this formal schooling. Actually, in my case, I think it was because my real-life experiences had educated me to levels beyond the book learning of my brothers and sister. I did learn from books that my mother would set me down with after dinner each day, but added practical life experiences. Frankly, I don't think I suffered for any lack of formal education. I could write, do fairly complex mathematics, had read some classics, and had a rudimentary understanding of American history – and Ireland's.

By age 19 and after four years in South Texas, I could lasso and tie a calf or just about any domestic critter with the best of men, shoe a horse, break a bronc, fairly accurately gauge the worth of beeves and horses, dress and butcher any game animal you could think of, could read the signs of impending rough weather, could track man or beast with the best men in the region, and felt as though I had a sixth sense for Comanche and Mexican banditos. By the way, out here in Texas, we learned to refer to cattle as beeves. Made sense to me. While he never expressed it in so many words, I think my father was bust-a-button proud of me and satisfied that he'd made the right decision in sending me to America as a mere 15-year-old. While I was close to my family, I was fully self-sufficient. Certainly, Long Larry would have been proud. I do know that my mother sent letters back to Kildare telling of our accomplishments in Texas.

THREE | IRISHMAN IN THE NUECES RIVER VALLEY

My brother Joe would graduate and, according to an article in the History of the Catholic Church in the Diocese of San Antonio, Texas, he would also teach at St. Mary's College for a time. The article reads, "During the Civil War, Mr. Joseph Dunn of Corpus Christi, Texas, rendered efficient aid as an instructor." It is with heavy heart that I share that Joe would pass away during the yellow fever epidemic that I'll write about later. Such were the uncertainties of life on the frontier.

In the early 1850s, there was not yet a Catholic church in Corpus Christi. The area was briefly served by a pastor from Victoria, Texas, County Mayo-born Father James Fitzgerald. A Dublin-born priest, Father Bernard O'Reilly, usually said Mass on Sundays at the home of Cornelius Cahill, a neighbor. They referred to Father O'Reilly as the "saddlebag priest," given his lack of a church home. He would occasionally stop in my father's home to spend the night and deliver Mass the next morning. I'd be remiss not to share that my father and my brother John were instrumental in the eventual establishment of St. Patrick's Church in Corpus Christi in 1857. Its first priest was Father O'Reilly. My father also gave over a portion of his land that later would become St. Theresa's Catholic Church, along what is today called Up River Road. As you've by now fully gathered, my family was very much involved in the Catholic Church and wrapped in their Christian faith.

My Uncle Peter's blacksmith business was sufficiently established that he brought his wife Margaret and their eight children to Corpus Christi. They sailed from Liverpool, England on August 4, 1852 on a ship named the Ellen Maria, first landing in New Orleans, Louisiana in late September and ultimately joining Uncle Peter in Corpus Christi on October 31. I can tell you first hand that Peter's family was amazed at the grandeur of the broad vistas of their adopted South Texas home with its seemingly endless and often cloudless blue skies. They quickly made themselves at home in the city. Colonel Kinney's dream was growing rapidly, and the Dunns of County Kildare had become part of it.

I enjoyed helping my father with a few head of the cattle he'd purchased. It afforded me a great opportunity to learn about how the longhorns behaved, what sort of care was needed – not much – and how to turn a few dollars with them. I found my way to folks in Corpus Christi involved in the cattle trade, where I began to learn about the business side of cattle. It was all about the markets, and how much was being paid. For example, the west coast might pay out more per head than the central plains, but the trip through the Rockies was expensive.

With four of Long Larry Dunn's five sons now fully ensconced in Texas, it was time for his grandchildren to get serious about settling down. I fully appreciated having my father and uncles around, as I had to grow up so much faster than most children my age. I was already considered an adult. Thinking about settling down was pretty much all I could do, as I devoted my time to learning ranching and the livestock speculating business from the ground up. I was passionate about it. I saved as much money as I could with the goal of buying my own spread. My father let me raise my own beeves, and I began to establish my reputation in the region as a reasonably savvy speculator. My father kept telling me that I had a natural gift for business. Notably, my peers thought of me as a skilled and fair negotiator. There were less-than-savory characters in the cattle business, but I really didn't worry about them given my growing reputation as a tough negotiator who could back up my word with a Colt revolver as needed.

I have to admit that about this time, I was experiencing a lot of restless nights. In fact, I began to have this recurring dream. I was herding longhorns. The entire dream found me in a saddle, yelling and cajoling the beasts to obey my will. In the mornings, I'd wake up sweaty and even a bit sore from thrashing about. The dreams evolved into being in a house with a stable and corral. Lord, but these dreams were vivid; they were alive. Imagine my surprise when I'd wake up in only my under garments.

I finally shared my dreams with my father and what I thought they meant. I mean, who better to talk with? I expect I shouldn't have been surprised at his response.

"Nicholas, my son, it is time. You need your own land to raise your own longhorns." He'd seen the passion growing in me.

Father stroked his chin thoughtfully. "I know there's property west of here. It's rough country but can be tamed. You're ready, you've saved, and I'm pleased to help. We can get your brothers to join in building a suitable house. I know your mother and sister Annie will be happy to help make it a home."

I recall feeling ever so grateful. My dream that night was a peaceful one. My days ahead would be filled with all that goes into acquiring property, choosing and purchasing livestock, building a house and outbuildings, and beginning to establish my spread as part of the local community. The freedom, the fulfillment of dreams, the destiny crafted by Long Larry Dunn would be realized.

A future had been laid out before me. While there were many good times experienced by the Dunn family here in South Texas, the times could be – as you will learn – also tragic and dangerous. It was untamed country, after all. Raw. Wild. Would we be up to it? Well, we were Texans!

FOUR

Settling Down

If you climb into the saddle, be ready for the ride.

Texas-ism

Life along the Nueces River and its tributaries was good, especially compared to the challenges the people faced in Ireland. Corpus Christi, and such civilization as it offered, was close at hand. The population had boomed to nearly 200 residents. Dirt streets spread westward from the bay, and commerce flourished despite the relatively shallow waters of the port. In fact, an efficient system of ferries and barges enabled cargo to be shuttled in from deep water boats. There were shipwrecks on occasion, but most sea traffic traded cargo with great success. Warehouses pretty much bulged with goods, and tradesmen, lawyers, bankers, and merchants fleshed out the population. As an example, my Uncle Peter's smithy business flourished. Here in America, we were masters of our own fates. It didn't take long to learn to be on the lookout for the many scalawags and other ne'er-do-wells that engaged in all manner of smuggling of contraband, rustling of livestock, and general mayhem. Mostly, the law wasn't up to reining the lawbreakers in, so citizens would form what were called vigilance committees. Justice was often at the end of a rope.

During these times, the availability of potable water – water you could drink and bathe in and cook with – was an ongoing concern. Mostly, we relied on rainwater collected in large cisterns. Each home, each ranch house, had its own "reservoir." When droughts occurred and cisterns ran low, we bought water from vendors called *ballileros,* who carted it into Corpus Christi and surrounding ranches and communities. There were many dry times, and the water vendors did a thriving business.

There was no such thing as indoor plumbing. We bucketed water from the cisterns or ran a pipe. Being somewhat creative, we would occasionally rig a shower, though we mostly used large tubs to bathe in – sometimes heating them over hot coals. For certain bodily functions, we built small shanty-like structures most folk called outhouses or privies. Having our own cistern and outhouse constituted high living on the South Texas frontier. As I shared earlier, my father built a two-holer – the height of luxury.

The immigrating Irish, of whom my family was but one, represented several clans – and I use that label purposefully, as the English invaders back home had outlawed the Irish family terms "clan" and "sect" roughly 300 years ago in a vain attempt to unify Ireland and dilute its heritage. My grandfather, Long Larry, insisted that we never yield our heritage to the English.

As I previously mentioned in having taken the advice from my Uncle Matt, I sought to improve my Spanish language ability. I found it especially useful. In fact, most of the family strove to learn it as much for facilitating trade opportunities as for protection. Miscommunication, after all, can lead to misunderstandings that can ultimately lead to missed opportunity or – of greater concern – conflict. Many of the Mexicans that chose to remain as residents in Texas after the war did make the effort to learn English. Actually, at any given time, we could be hearing all sorts of languages and variants from the twangy drawl of the Texans to the Indian-Spanish Mestizo dialect of the *vaqueros* to the remaining Irish lilt to a touch of Creole from French traders out of New Orleans to the German and Dutch traders mostly settled in the central parts of Texas. It was a diverse population, driven by a combination of economic opportunity and self-protection. Importantly, all were welcome so long as they stayed within the law.

Our Catholic faith easily integrated with the pre-existing Spanish culture as they, too, were mostly Catholic. We were a God-fearing lot, good Catholics to the bone. My father was the right-hand man of the bishops, priests, and sisters of the parish. I understood that, at one time or another, virtually all of the Sacraments had been delivered in my father's house except Holy Orders. In any case, be assured that I recited the Rosary every morning on the gallery of the house on my own ranch as the sun peeked up over the eastern horizon.

I should add, however, that it wasn't always smooth so far as race and religion were concerned. Many folks were blinded by prejudice. There were instances of priests being harassed and even killed. Negroes were pretty much ill-treated leading up to and through the eventuality of the War Between the States. Texans of Mexican heritage were often treated as non-people, lower in some folks' minds than the Negro slaves.

Long about mid-1855, my father shared a letter he'd received from my Uncle Patrick back in County Kildare. Long Larry had passed away the previous year after a sudden illness. Patrick indicated that he'd be staying back to care for my grandmother and that she was moving to Dublin. We expected that Patrick would eventually join us in Texas, but it turned out that would be a few years yet. I was of the opinion that Long Larry had reached a place where he would be eternally happy. I imagined that God would see to it that Long Larry's dreams of adventure were fulfilled forever. Given that Long Larry had passed away quite a while ago, we held a wake in Corpus Christi in his honor. By my judgment, any grieving was not so great as if we had been by his death bed and at his funeral. Whiskey flowed, and life in Texas went on.

It's important to mention that while I didn't participate so much in politics, my Irish brethren regularly served as elected Corpus Christi city leaders right on through the War Between the States and well into the 1880s.

After my original smaller foray into ranching as aided by my father, I soon acquired about 12,000 acres of lush prairie roughly 12 miles or so west of Corpus Christi and east of what would, about 35 years later, become the town of Alice. That town would be named after the daughter of Richard King. Keep in mind that King had established the 825,000-acre – and now famous – King Ranch around 1853.

The King Ranch is not to be ignored in any history of South Texas, and the Dunn family did pay it some well-deserved attention. Captain Richard King and Gideon Lewis were its founders. It was so large as to stretch into six Texas counties. King, born in New York City to Irish immigrants, had been a river pilot. He served under General Zachary Taylor, operating steamboats from Brazos Santiago Harbor to Matamoros, Mexico. King made a good living after the war hauling merchandise on the Rio Grande.

On a trip to Corpus Christi to see Colonel Kinney's Lone Star Fair, he laid eyes on Santa Gertrudis Creek about 125 miles from the Rio Grande. For King, it was a majestic vision. I can imagine Richard King sitting astride his horse standing in lush stirrup-high grass, gazing out at the vista of what Mexicans called "Desert of the Dead," and envisioning thousands of head of grazing beeves. With plentiful shade from mesquite tree and live oak mottes, he fell in love with the property. King partnered with Texas Ranger Captain Gideon K. "Legs" Lewis and purchased the 15,500-acre *Rincón de Santa Gertrudis* grant. King and Lewis gradually expanded their holdings, eventually totaling 1.2 million acres. As I understood it, Lewis was killed in 1855 by the husband of a woman with whom he had been having an affair. Lesson learned, I expect. King subsequently further consolidated his land holdings and raised his trademark longhorns as well as Brahmans, Herefords, and Beef Shorthorns. Eventually, he'd breed his famous Santa Gertrudis breed.

Horses, sheep, and goats were also bred and raised. In fact, King Ranch quarter horses were highly sought after. The first official brands were registered in 1859, though the famous "Running W" wouldn't be registered until after the War Between the States. It was an impressive undertaking. I could aspire to such holdings, but I honestly didn't have the breadth of business sense to match Richard King.

Of note was a method King used to manage costs. Given the size of his herds, taking them to market was a costly undertaking. King made his trail bosses owners of the herd, signing a note for the beeves, driving them to market (a 100-day task), and selling them to the northern buyers, thereby relieving their indebtedness and earning a tidy profit that served as wages.

As a 23-year-old-man, I was fully immersed in the cattle business. If you're not acquainted with the chancy game of cattle speculation, allow me to share just a bit. I did look up the Latin root for speculate, and it apparently comes from the word *peculium*, meaning private property. The *pecu* part of the word actually means cattle, a commodity considered of great value since ancient times. Of course, speculate – despite its Latin root – does not of itself have anything to do with cattle. Confused? Anyway, speculation is like a game of skill; it's about finding the underlying value and matching it against the underlying demand of buyers and sellers of the commodity – beeves in my case. This is balanced against the time entailed in the development of the market. If you don't understand what I'm saying, don't fret. It's complicated and takes an iron constitution. Recall that the Nueces Strip was home to millions of horses, buffalo, and longhorns. With abundant grasses to chow down on, the beasts weren't inclined to go hungry.

Oh, now and again you'll hear the words beeves or cattle. They are the same thing, only we cowboys think of the cattle that produce beef for your dining pleasure as beeves. The terms are interchangeable. Makes sense, doesn't it? Just sayin'. Oh, and just to add a bit more to your lexicon, most of the beeves driven north were steers. The castration that turned bulls into steers tended to fatten them up and make them more valuable pound for pound in the marketplace. Considering how naturally wiry longhorns were, any fattening up was a blessing.

Fences were virtually unknown in Texas, especially on the Nueces Strip. Cattle were free to roam whenever and wherever they chose. This made it especially challenging to maintain herds. Cattle were branded to identify their owner. To be official, brands had to be registered in the county of record and all sales recorded in the county's Stock Recorded Book. This system depended on honorable men. Would that they were all honorable.

In rounding up beeves for market, a rancher might find a dozen or more different brands in a herd of merely a couple of hundred cattle. If the rancher sold cattle belonging to another rancher, he was responsible for paying the rancher whatever price he'd gotten less a dollar fee he was able to keep for his trouble.

Aside from the rigors of herding cattle and the natural dangers of the prairie, rustlers preyed on the wide-ranging tendencies of the longhorns. Altering brands or outright herding beeves to remote locales occurred all too often. Little wonder that rustling became a hanging offense.

Back in the early 1850s, it's notable that the market in beeves was affected by a tick-borne illness called "Texas fever." While the longhorns had built immunity to this "cattle tick fever," mid-western beeves in Missouri, Kansas, and Ohio fell victim to the illness to the extent that those state legislatures passed legislation to quarantine their states against "southern" beeves. As you might imagine, that had some major impact on the speculation business, not to mention changing the routes of the major drive trails like the Chisholm and the Western. Significant outcomes from cattle tick fever were a period of fewer drives northward along those traditional trails and the eventual rapid growth of the meat packing business in the nearby Texas port cities. Meanwhile, alternatives opened up, such as the flourishing market in the California gold fields.

Keep in mind, too, that this was an age of open range. There were seas of prairie grass waving in the breezes. Shrubs were not so plentiful, as there was an ongoing battle between grass-fed prairie fires and mesquite growth. The mesquite would eventually flourish, as roads and wagon trails formed firebreaks of sorts. Raising beeves and horses were natural pursuits on this prairie, as it mostly seemed as though you could see for miles and thus keep an eye on your herds. Barbed wire wouldn't even be invented by a fella named Glidden until 1874, so the range was open, and primary concerns were favorable grazing sites and ability to control the supply of water. Both were plentiful.

On the upside, living miles away from more densely populated places like Corpus Christi pretty much spared me the ravages of diseases like yellow fever, cholera, and small pox. But my isolation made me vulnerable to marauding Mexican bandits, Anglo thugs, and ever-present Indians. While Mexican bandits were to be feared, the Comanche were feared worse, both because they moved at night and they were ruthless killers. Blessedly for me, the Karankawa tribe stayed closer to the coast and didn't stray inland so much. They were rumored to be cannibalistic so far as disposing of captured enemies.

The dangers were topped off by all manner of dangerous wildlife, from javelina to wolves, coyotes, rattlesnakes, and even mountain lions.

I guess you could say my ranch was isolated. I did get to see family from time to time, but mostly I hired *vaqueros* to help with livestock chores. Neighbors tended to live a day's ride or so apart. I worked from sunup to sundown. That was the work ethic of the cowboy. We kept cool by keeping windows open to capture evening breezes, though we kept the lights dim to discourage insect pests. Bats seemed to be our major defensive weapon against mosquitoes. The little flying beasts were voracious eaters of mosquitos. Sometimes, there'd be enough bats filling the evening sky to temporarily block out the moonlight.

One of my favorite pastimes was to venture out from my house in the evening. It seemed as though you could see stars forever. Aside from an occasional hoot from an owl, you could almost hear those stars blinking on and off as they twinkled. Night on the Texas prairie was indeed an incredibly majestic place to be. God had given Texas an awesome gift.

I raised my own beeves, as well as horses. I had the potential to play both ends of the speculation game. In fact, locally, I found that I could impact the speculative market in my favor ever so slightly based upon how I timed the sale of my own cattle. I should add that horses were plentiful across the Texas plains, and I was finding some success breeding them as well. Finding quality horses was a challenge, so I strove to meet the need as best I could. The wild mustangs of the open prairie were not considered prime stock. I heard that the Texas Rangers used to complain about the nags they were issued compared to the relatively prime horseflesh supposedly ridden by the U.S. Cavalry. Then again, that was debatable if you'd listen to the complaints of soldiers.

Speaking of cavalry, it's notable that the 2nd U.S. Cavalry, intended for duty protecting South Texas, had been transferred to Utah to fight Indians. Far to the south of my ranch, there was an increasing problem with Lipan Apache stealing livestock from and attacking Texas ranches after which they'd escape to Mexico. Bowing to public demand for retaliation, Governor Pease commissioned and got funding for a Texas Ranger company under James Callahan. Captain Callahan, with a company of 130 Rangers, followed the Apache right into Mexico. After crossing the Rio Grande at Eagle Pass, Callahan engaged the Apache near Piedras Negras. There, the savages were reinforced by Mexican troops. This had become a more formidable force. After looting and burning Piedra Negras to teach a lesson, the Texas Rangers wound up re-crossing back into Texas after what I'd heard was an inconclusive battle. The Apache problem really wouldn't be resolved for another couple of years.

I will say that it was reassuring to know that Texas could muster the forces to defend itself. The outcome was less concerning to me than the effort. After living an essentially defenseless life in Ireland, it was a blessing to be here where we had the freedom to defend ourselves.

I heard reports that the notorious Mexican bandit Cheno Cortino was lurking around with designs on Corpus Christi. It's notable that Mexico was enduring its own civil war in the late 1850s. As I recall, the big names were a liberal rabble-rouser named Benito Juarez versus the "Mexican Robin Hood" Juan Nepomuceno Cortina Goseacochea, who led bands of vigilantes, not to mention a bunch of cattle thieves. Cortina was also nicknamed the Red Robber of the Rio Grande, and Cheno Cortina. Given the difficulty pronouncing his full name, it was a blessing that he had those nicknames.

Cheno Cortina had achieved the rank of brigadier general in the Mexican Army during the Mexican-American War. It was said by some that Cortina was the "first socially motivated border bandit." The Juarez vs. Cortina internal squabbles would occasionally bleed over north of the Rio Grande for the next decade or so, much to the chagrin of those peaceful Mexicans who'd settled in Texas. Civil wars and vigilantes seemed to be a given in this era of lawlessness and radical social upheaval. One of the quite grisly aspects of these flare-ups was a practice that actually spanned more than a half dozen decades: lynchings. Hemp parties, necktie parties, or whatever folks cared to call them, were seen as an efficient way to mete out justice. Given that prejudice ran deep in some quarters, hanging some ethnicities was akin to killing non-humans. It wasn't uncommon to see Mexican cattle thieves strung up from a tree along the trail. They most likely weren't afforded a trial, and it's highly probable that many innocent men met their fates this way.

To place Cortina in perspective, there had been reports that he'd come over from Mexico several times beginning in 1859, raiding mostly in the Brownsville area where his mother owned a ranch. Corpus Christi began to face up to the possibility of Cortina turning his attention northward and formed a defense unit called Walker's Mounted Rifles. My uncle Peter Dunn served as farrier to keep their hundred or so horses shod. After all their careful exercises and drills, no attack came, and the War Between the States would intervene right soon. I gave serious consideration to joining up with Walker's Mounted Rifles, but was focused on my avocation.

I was first and foremost a rancher, a cowboy, a cattleman. I don't mean to make it sound as though I had outsized or unfair influence over the livestock speculation game, but I was able to do quite well for a time in South Texas. To put it in perspective, there were somewhere between three and six million head of longhorns grazing around all of Texas at this time. With Texas being so large and the cattle – especially the promiscuous longhorns – breeding in record numbers across wide expanses of grazing land, it was little wonder that the cattle business and speculation in them were thriving. There were just as many horses, too, but the folks back east didn't consider them so good to eat.

I guess so long as I'm talking about livestock speculation and such, it might be of value to understand how the famed Texas longhorn came about. As I understand it, the Texas longhorn descended from long-horned cattle brought by Spanish settlers with Christopher Columbus in 1493. The cattle were apparently native to the Iberian Peninsula in Europe, also known as Spain. While some historians are of a mind to believe that at least one line of longhorns descended from the British Blakewell stock, the Spanish origins are most widely accepted. The Iberian-lineage longhorns originally made it to the San Antonio Valley region of Texas, thanks to Franciscan missionaries as they sought to establish a string of missions northward from Vera Cruz to civilize the Indians and encourage Spanish settlement. As the influence of the missions waned over time, the cattle escaped to the prairies and multiplied prolifically.

Attempts would eventually be made to cross-breed the longhorns with other breeds to bulk them up and make them a meatier breed, but those efforts mostly failed. That's why Richard King eventually bred those Santa Gertrudis beeves that lacked the breadth of horns but packed on plenty of meat. In any case, longhorn beeves have been known to reach as much as 2,000 pounds with tip-to-tip horn spreads of more than 100 inches. In my humble experience, 1,200 to 1,400 pounds was far more common, and it could take upward of five years to attain the sort of horn spread the breed is famous for.

The longhorn's high fertility, disease resistance, longevity, heartiness, and ability to graze among coarse forage made them a preferable breed for the South Texas range. Despite being only a couple of generations removed from the wild, they can be made reasonably tame. Still, you must be careful of accidentally getting in the way of those horns. If these longhorns are removed from human contact for a year or so, they can quickly get quite wild and nasty to deal with.

I should add that while people most often think of longhorns when referring to the beeves business in Texas, there was considerable success breeding Brahmans. The Brahman – noted for the large hump over its shoulders – were native to India and imported – or more accurately, smuggled – initially into Louisiana and thence to Texas in the 1850s and 1860s. The Brahman is well-suited to the South Texas heat, resistant to insect pests, and can travel considerable distances without water. A typical bull weighs between 1,600 and 2,200 pounds at maturity, with cows weighing in at several hundred pounds less.

They were bred to achieve better heat resistance versus the Herefords.

Anyway, this serves to give you a bit of background about my business.

The speculation business was ever more successful, and I saved a fair amount of money. From time to time, I would stretch my hunting ventures to the west to investigate what additional land might be available to continue to build out my ranch. I was always on guard, having heard tales of Comanche ambushes and – as I've said before – the horrible ways they treated captives. I've mentioned Comanche a few times, and it might be helpful to grasping their nature by understanding their name. I hear tell that the name Comanche is derived from a Ute tribe word *kumantsi*, roughly meaning anyone that wants to fight all the time. The Comanche were barbaric enough to have chased the feared Apache south ahead of their murderous sweep across the plains. So the name alone gives you a hint at what settlers on the Texas frontier dealt with. I was always on guard. After all, I rather liked my red hair and hoped to keep it for a while. The thought of my hair decorating a Comanche lance was not exactly attractive.

I took quite readily to raising my own beeves. With those 12,000 acres, I didn't lack for land and grazing. Before I knew it, I had several hundred head. This is likely as good a point as any to describe how we got cattle to market and made the money we needed to operate the ranch. I should add that driving beeves to market wasn't nearly so romantic as those dime-store novelists made it out to be.

With my speculating, I had heard about the incredible prices being offered in San Francisco with the opening of the gold fields. A head of beef worth $5 in Texas sold for $100 in California. Of course, it generally took five to six months to drive beeves from Texas to San Francisco. Those dang Rocky Mountains got in the way. The same could be said for drives to mining operations in places like Montana.

It figures that, by the time I had raised enough longhorns to make an economically sensible drive to the West coast, they were experiencing a glut of beeves out there and prices were dropping precipitously. I talked it over at length with my father and my brothers John and Michael, and we decided to send our longhorns north on the Shawnee Trail to Kansas and Missouri where they could be fattened up for market sale and shipped east.

Drives normally began in the spring. We'd brand our beeves, as they'd be combined with other ranchers' herds for the drive. Some ranchers clipped notches in a distinguishing pattern in the ears of their beeves rather than, or in addition to, branding. Keep in mind, too, that longhorns were plentiful throughout Texas. We could count on coming upon wild, unbranded cattle from time to time. They could be especially annoying for a variety of reasons from luring cows away to goring our horses. Recall that longhorns in the Texas wilds were fully self-sufficient beasts. I've seen the carcasses of bears, wolves, and panthers that found themselves on the losing end of fights with longhorns.

Typically, I'd corral about 400 head. The main herd was assembled up north of San Patricio and east of San Antonio until there'd be around 2,500 head or so. That actually would be an unusually large herd. A 10- to 12-man crew of drovers and drivers could handle a herd that size if they were truly savvy cowboys. Each man supplied his own outfit, including at least three horses each. A horse wrangler would be responsible for watching over the *remuda* of spare horses. Personally speaking, I was partial to the Mexican cowboys or *vaqueros*. Notably, there were even a few adventurous women drovers who disguised themselves as boys to join the drives at minimum pay. With rough cowboys on the trail, their lives and what might exist of their chastity depended on maintaining their disguises.

Upon arrival at the drive destination, sales were made, ownership documentation transferred, and the crews pretty much went their separate ways until the next season. Typically, we might lose upward of 25 percent of our herd to the hazards of the trail.

Drives required a commitment. A typical drive might cover 10 to 15 miles a day and last one to three months depending on delays from storms, floods, droughts, stampedes, and Kiowa or Comanche raids. Running the beeves too hard resulted in weight loss, so the idea was to permit the herd to rest enough to maintain weight.

I must admit that, while I loved my horses, I found the longhorns fascinating. Like horses, there was a mental affinity that drovers acquired to effectively drive the beeves. Just watching them bed down reminds me of a dog as it finds the most comfortable sleep position. The longhorns look to make themselves as comfortable as possible lying in the prairie dust. I learned to listen for steady breathing. If a longhorn lifts its head, curls up his nose, and takes a long sniff, it's a sign that there might be trouble brewing.

Understand that these beeves could be spooked by any number of sights, sounds, or smells. While I mostly stayed at my ranch to breed and care for my own beeves, I did join enough of the drives to be able to give you a visual picture of hundreds of beeves stretched out for two or three miles on the trail as they followed the lead beeves. During hot weather, it was preferable for the herd to be strung out as it kept the beeves cooler than when they bunched up. A trail boss – paid roughly $125 per month – ran the drive. The crew would typically be spread from the head of the herd to the end with a couple of outriders in pairs on the flanks. Communications were mostly by hand signals, as there was constant noise from longhorns and horses.

The most important crew member after the trail boss was the cook. The cook had a challenging job, given that the legendary chuck wagon wasn't invented yet. I must add that calves born on the trail drives were usually killed, as they were unable to keep up with the adults. I'm getting ahead of myself here, but – lest you be put off by the seeming heartlessness of killing newborn beeves – by the late 1860s, calves were often being gathered in a wagon during the day and released each night to their mothers. I also found the bond between a cow and her calf to be fascinating. Back on my spread, I found the protective nature of the cow especially notable, as she'd go to great lengths to hide the younger critters from predators. You didn't want to be a varmint threatening the calf of a longhorn cow. The longhorn was quite adept at using those long horns. If I was in a blarney mind, I'd say they could put a horn tip through the eye of a needle without half trying. That's a stretch, but you get my point.

Well, as I said, I did go on a couple of drives and I expect I ought to share a sense of what it was like. In the first place, I couldn't just drop everything and go off on a trail drive. I had to arrange for someone to keep an eye on the ranch, usually my brother Michael. I didn't cotton much to coming home to find beeves rustled or my house robbed or the like. A lot of bad stuff could happen during the couple of months away.

One drive of note back in 1856 was especially marked by fear of Comanche. Seems that with the U.S. 2nd Cavalry transferred to Utah (as I described earlier), the Comanche had become an increasing problem. The Penateka Comanche chief Buffalo Hump didn't want to stay in the land reserved for his tribe. It was a tough blow to Texas ranchers that we didn't take kindly to. While Captain Callahan had squelched the Lipan Apache problem in South Texas by running them off to Mexico, there was no commensurate attempt to protect us from Comanche. Our drives mostly ran along or just east of Comancheria territory. I'll talk more about that later, but the borders of the Comancheria just about split Texas in half. To the west lurked danger and to the east a little less danger.

With that as background, I was outriding at the mid-section of the herd one afternoon. Of a sudden, there was a shout. "Look to your guns, men! We're under attack!" Comanche, maybe a dozen or more, appeared as if from nowhere. Now, I remind you that I was protective of my scalp as much as the next drover. It was essential to our mutual protection that we work together in these situations.

My Colt found its way into my hand, and I vividly recall shooting the first Comanche I saw right off his pony. The look of pained helpless surprise on that warrior's face as the slug tore through his chest sent a chill up my spine. Despite the excitement of battle, I couldn't help but feel a touch of regret that the Comanche had chosen their thieving and killing ways. I didn't have time to dwell on that.

The Comanche were mostly after our horses, as they had some sort of inbred dislike of longhorns. As we returned fire, they peeled back. Their strategy was for us to follow them to where we'd be ambushed, and they could steal our horses at leisure. I yelled, "Hold back. Protect the horses!'

The trail boss echoed my shouts. "Hold, men! Let 'em run!" he ordered. He looked around, taking stock of the situation. "Anyone hurt?" He noted that all the saddles were filled with drovers, and nobody admitted to being a pincushion for Comanche arrows.

The Comanche were surely watching and were just as surely disappointed. We'd fought them off this time, though we'd need to set out extra watch at night. Turns out the Comanche especially loved to steal horses at night. Vigilance would be our lot.

I've never been quite sure how I felt about Comanche. While they were to be admired as warriors, their culture of killing their many enemies – including other Comanche – was a worry. Had I any loved ones on my ranch at the time, it would surely have made me far more protective. There was something to be said for not being married, as I had great freedom to build a productive life on the Nueces Strip that would contribute to me eventually marrying and having a family. I do have to admit that I was starting to think about raising a family of my own. But I wasn't done with the excitement of droving cattle to market and building this part of my life in Texas.

Another drive of note began up east of San Antonio in the spring of 1859, headed up the Shawnee Trail to Sedalia, Missouri. The winter had been warmer than most, and it appeared that we'd be blessed in the spring with a dry spell. Two of my *vaqueros*, Jorge and Juan, volunteered to help me drive about 300 head of beeves northward to the herd assembly area. We each brought four horses. Our saddle gear included oilskin drover duster, blanket roll, a new .54 caliber 1859 Sharps rifle, a .44 caliber Colt six-shooter, lariat, quirt, and a tin cup and plate. I wore a black wide-brimmed hat and completed my outfit with leggings (some call them chaps), good tight-fitting boots, spurs, bandana, gloves, shirt, and vest. Efficiency was a key, so everything we took on a drive had a purpose. The ubiquitous bandana had multiple uses including filtering dust, cooling heated bodies, blindfolding skittish horses, binding wounds, and screening from the sun. Good boots and leggings were a must to protect our legs from the brush, cactus, tree branches, and rattlesnakes we'd likely encounter on the trail. I've even heard of good boots and leggings deflecting the horns of a charging longhorn. Of course, that didn't help the horse much. Keep in mind, this stuff would be worn for several weeks, so I packed an extra shirt and pants. Guess we smelled as bad as the herd.

We joined up with about 1,500 head of longhorns and, after a couple of days of grazing and rest, we departed on the trail in early April. Try to visualize the constant dust kicked up by the cattle, the occasional shouts of *vaqueros* as they darted about to keep the herd on the trail, and the grunting and bellowing of the bulls. At night, there'd be the singing of all sorts of songs aimed at soothing the skittish beeves. We made it through Austin and headed toward Waco, following this old Indian trail. We were perhaps a day out of Austin when the rains hit. Clouds had been gathering, but we had surely underestimated what was to come. The sky opened up, and it was all we could do to circle the herd. The wind drove the rain clean through our oil-skin dusters, so we were quickly drenched. We lucked out in that the little lightning we had was far enough off to not upset the herd. Longhorns could be especially upset around lightning. We worried about flash floods, but were lucky on that account, too.

Next morning the sun peeked out, the cook mustered up some grub, and we set a few fires to dry ourselves out and take the early spring chill off. We had barely restarted the drive when a strange feeling came upon me that was enough to raise the hairs on the back of my neck. I'd learned to pay attention to these sorts of signals of things not being quite right. Sure enough, at least three dozen Comanche appeared seemingly from nowhere.

The savages were close enough that we could just about smell them in the heavy dew-filled early morning air. They paused before descending upon us with their war whoops. I had good recollection of the attack we'd dealt with a couple of years before so had a pretty fair idea of what to do besides shoot back. A half-dozen of the hostiles initially headed directly toward us, whooping and hollering – an old Comanche tactic used to fully engage their victims before drawing them into a trap.

I recall that there were twelve of us drovers, and our herd was strung out for about two miles. Outnumbered three to one, we would be easy targets to pick off one by one. The trail boss and two of our lead drovers joined me and my *vaqueros,* and we decided at the full gallop to employ the Texas Ranger strategy of aggressive attack. The Rangers had proven that tactic back in the 1840s, and Texas Ranger Captain Rip Ford had been applying it recently to fighting Comanche for a couple of years now up on the Canadian and Brazos Rivers. We headed toward the Comanche with our pistols blazing and quickly ran them down, including the bunch that lay in ambush. But, they won – sort of.

While we attacked the main band, a few of them snuck behind and made off with nearly a dozen of our horses that we could ill afford to lose. That was certainly a wrinkle in our own strategy, and we should have known better. Admittedly, in the heat of the initial attack by the Comanche, I'd forgotten our success in protecting our *remuda* of horses on previous drives. Importantly, none of us got hurt, and we managed to kill or wound three or four Comanche. The entire incident would make for great campfire chatter for the rest of the drive, as we became ever-braver Indian fighters in word if not deed.

As I recall, the trail boss was quite grateful to me personally for leading the fight against the Comanche. He was a talker, so I expect some enhancements to my growing reputation as an Indian fighter might be attributed to him.

After being hit with a gully-washer of a rainstorm and then by Comanche, we had to believe that the remainder of the drive couldn't possibly be so bad. We made it up past the Red River and Shawnee Hills. Nary a day went by that we didn't kill a varmint or two, as rattlesnakes, coyotes, and the like were plentiful. And rattlesnake meat was actually very tasty. Our cook must have known at least a dozen ways to serve up rattlers.

I'd be remiss not to share a cowboy technique called tailing. Occasionally, a longhorn would get itself riled up and decide to leave the herd. He'd head for the nearest thicket of grass or brush, and it was up to alert drovers to fetch the beast. The *vaquero* would haul off after the longhorn at a gallop. He'd pull alongside, reach down, grab the tip of the longhorn's very long tail, and wrap it around his saddle horn as he applied the brakes to his horse. The longhorn would usually land on its belly with a whump and cloud of dust. The stunned beast might lie there for a few moments, gathering its wits before trotting back to the herd, having forgotten why it left.

Tailing worked most of the time, but I saw at least one instance where the poor horse ran afoul of the longhorn's dangerous horns. It was tough to see a fine mount have to be put down. Occasionally, the cowboy would get himself hurt, too, though rarely were they put down.

Speaking of rattlesnakes, an incident I faced with a rattler was just a bit unnerving. I woke up one morning, my head still propped against my saddle and spied a rattler to my left not more than five or six feet away. That snake had been slithering along pretty much minding its own business when it spied me. There he sat, looking at me through those squinty snake eyes. The morning sun reflected from his long scaly body as he began to coil himself. I judged him at about six feet of pure venom. Dang, but he looked to be the very embodiment of evil! Little wonder a snake was chosen to wreak evil in the Garden of Eden.

My right hand slowly wrapped around my Walker Colt, and I eased it very slowly up across my chest. By this time, the rattler had taken further note and was deciding whether to fight or escape. I'm not sure what goes through a rattlesnake's brain, but I doubt it was anything good. To make it all complicated, my *vaquero* friend, Jorge, was about ten feet on the other side of the snake. If I was to shoot, I'd have to be especially accurate so as not to hit Jorge. A bead of sweat found its way into my eye. I squinted as the salt stung my eyes. A shard of morning sunlight exploded on my gun barrel, startling the snake. In the span of maybe five seconds, the rattler raised its head, started its warning rattling, and I squeezed the trigger. The bullet blew its head clean off.

"*Santa mierda!*" shouted Jorge as he sat bolt upright, not yet realizing that a bullet had whizzed by him within inches while he slept. I'll spare everyone the English translation.

"*Buenas dias, amigo. Gran dia para vivir.*" I told him what a great day it was to be alive, smiled broadly, slicked back my red hair, put on my hat, uncurled from my bedroll, and tossed the rattler's body over to Jorge. The cook grabbed up the thing, as it was a delicacy that could be added to this day's chili.

By this time, everyone else had been awakened by the shot and came running. They were impressed with my marksmanship, but it wasn't until a few days later that I told Jorge just how good that shot had to be. I didn't dare tell him that I wasn't able to lift the Colt high enough to sight down the barrel. I have little doubt that this experience with the rattlesnake combined with killing Comanche on trail drives contributed to my reputation as marksman and Indian fighter. I'm not judging whether that's good or bad; it was simply the way it was.

Speaking of rattlesnakes, I'd be remiss if I didn't mention the grub on these drives. The cook had to be especially resourceful. A popular dish was chili, popular because the ingredients might be just about anything so long as the flavor was dominated by seasonings. Every good cook stocked chili pepper. While beef and venison were dominant meats for most chili, the cook occasionally took license, and we'd be treated to rabbit, prairie dog, coyote, the ubiquitous rattlesnake, or whatever critters the cook was up to shooting to throw into the cooking pot. Most drovers had cast-iron stomachs, so it didn't much matter what the cook used in his recipes. Besides, hunger makes most anything seem tastier.

One final note about those rattlesnakes. Their venom was nasty, to say the least. Nasty enough to kill most men. There was a cure of sorts that I've never had the opportunity to prove or disprove. It was said that the leaves of the Spanish Dagger plant stabbed into a rattlesnake wound lessened the effect of the venom. Of course, I hear tell that cutting the snake bite and sucking blood can be effective unless you have any sort of wounds in your mouth. Bottom line by my way of thinking is to simply try to avoid those slithering serpents. If the snake was bad enough to symbolize evil in the Garden of Eden, who am I to suggest otherwise?

After the Red River, we made great time across the prairies. We did encounter a bit of a greeting committee of sorts as we approached Missouri. It seems these so-called "vigilance committees" were showing up ever more frequently owing to the fear of Texas fever, that tick-borne disease that our longhorns had built up an immunity to. On occasion, these encounters turned bad with both beeves and drovers getting killed. In our case, we managed to negotiate our way to a slight change in our route that looped around these folks' ranches.

Finally, we reached Sedalia. We drove our herd of bawling raucous beeves to the stockyards. It's as though the beasts knew their fate. We sold the herd – nearly all of them had made it – and did a bit of celebrating before heading home. Jorge and Juan showed me a great place to eat in Sedalia, and we all got cleaned up and enjoyed real beds for a couple of nights. It was quite a contrast compared to being on the trail. There was an incident that I feel obliged to share.

In my trips to Corpus Christi, I learned to play poker. Turns out, it was a popular game in the saloons of Sedalia. It should come of little surprise that I found myself a game. I sat with a couple of drovers from another outfit. We'd all been paid, had some strong drink, and had tales to share.

The dealer was a fellow who said his name was Bland Johnson. From his fancy clothes, I gathered him to be experienced at cards. There were several folks in the saloon. Some sat at the bar talking with the mostly pretty girls that hung out there. I must say, those girls could have used more clothing.

Johnson dealt. I'd learned in Corpus Christi to keep an eye on the dealer's hands, not his eyes. Cheaters depended on distracting their victims.

I'd already spotted the pearl handle of a revolver holstered under Johnson's shoulder. My Colt Walker remained secure at my side, though I had no reason to think I'd need it.

We were into our fourth round of dealing when the drover next to me pushed back from the table.

Johnson gave the man a steely-eyed look. "There a problem, cowboy?"

"I saw that card come out of your sleeve."

"You sayin' I'm a cheat?"

I found myself beginning to inch away. If there was to be any gunfire, I didn't want to be close. I moved my hand to my holstered Colt just in case.

"You sayin' you didn't cheat? You've been cheatin' near every hand."

The drover went for his gun, but hadn't even cleared leather when Johnson's revolver was already in his hand and pointed at the man's chest. "Don't!" was all Johnson said. He said it firmly, even-tempered as could be.

I had to admire Johnson's restraint. He could have killed the man right then and there. He knew the guy had been drinking and his judgment was impaired.

The drover released his weapon and very slowly lifted his hand. It was a tough call, as he had to trust Johnson, and trust was not an easily offered or accepted commodity in Texas in 1859.

Johnson then showed the drover what he'd thought was cheating. It was tricky, but was simply a show of card playing dexterity that most folks didn't ever see. No card had emerged from his sleeve, but someone could mistakenly think it did. "You wouldn't want killing over this, would you?" Johnson repeated the card trick. Johnson had the sense to see that a couple of the drovers were far too drunk to be playing, so he had begun to toy with them. He had no intention of taking their money. I must say that Johnson was an exception in the card hustling profession.

Everyone breathed easier. The cowboy apologized and pulled his chair back to the table. He didn't last but another round of play, though, before deciding not to lose any more of his hard-earned money. Johnson counted out roughly what the cowboy had lost and handed it to him. The drunken cowboy smiled sheepishly and managed to slur out a thank you.

In retrospect, I was pleased not to have been called upon to take any heroic action myself. It was a lesson in being certain of your circumstances before taking drastic action.

Cattle drives continued, and I worked them whenever I could. The Shawnee Trail up into Missouri wasn't much used once the War Between the States started and would be pretty much replaced by the Western Trail from Bandera to Dodge City and the Goodnight-Loving Trail out of San Angelo to Denver by the mid-1860s. Actually, Oliver Loving would be killed by Comanche in 1867, but Goodnight went on to amass a fortune in land and beeves. The famous Chisholm Trail meandered north from San Antonio, though some folks insisted that it actually began at the Red River. Supposedly named after a half-breed Scotch/Cherokee from Tennessee named Jesse Chisholm, it would carry millions of head of Texas beeves to Elsworth and Abilene,

Kansas. About the time the War Between the States ended, Texas had become a tougher place to live, with a hurting economy exacerbated by seriously under-maintained railroads and many unemployed Confederate veterans. The only thing there wasn't a shortage of was longhorns, and they were fetching attractive prices in the eastern markets.

Within a couple of decades, the famous Texas trails would meet their end as the range became crisscrossed with barbed wire and alternative transportation came into play. Cowboys incidentally often referred to barbed wire as "bob wire." Seems it was easier to trip off a dry tongue on the prairie and sipping a whiskey. In any case, the railroads would bring greater efficiency and lower cost in getting beef to market.

Oh, and it wouldn't be long before sheep ranching came into vogue in Nueces County. While the fertile soil was great for cotton, wool production began to rival it for commercial opportunity. Sheep soon outnumbered cattle by three to one, as they required less acreage to raise and were sort of a renewable resource despite that legendary promiscuity of longhorns. However, fenced land would also eventually lead to a decline in the sheep industry.

It's notable that livestock at this time far outnumbered people. The railroads and barbed wire were sort of a two-edged sword that had the effect of placing a greater premium on land and water rights and finding efficient ways of moving beeves to market.

We kept a close eye on the goings-on with the War Between the States. In the course of following the goings-on, we received some saddening news about this time. Our beloved Sam Houston passed away on July 26, 1863 after a long illness. I found myself especially saddened, given that he'd been removed from the governorship back in 1861 for his opposition to joining the Confederacy. He'd been a great citizen of Texas, serving state and republic as a true leader.

Whether as a military leader or as statesman, I fully admired the man. I hoped that saner heads might eventually prevail, and Texas would fully recognize his contributions.

I'll be devoting much of a chapter to yellow fever later on, but we did deal with bouts of the disease from time to time. No one knew how to treat yellow fever, and the medical folks of the time believed that administering warm liquids such as tea and keeping sufferers in confinement would work. Yellow fever did catch up with me, and I wound up joining Matt, Mike, John, Jr. and his daughter Annie, and his nephew "Red John" Dunn at my father's home. The Belgian hired man also contracted the disease. It seemed that misery loved company. We lay in fever for several days imbibing only hot liquids. Tragically, the Belgian hired hand passed away. The disease also took my Uncle Thomas, a fairly young man of 51 years with a large family. I had immigrated from Ireland with him in 1850 so found myself especially grieved at the loss.

Blessedly, as it turns out, it began to rain. It had a cooling effect. "Red John" threw open a window and held out a cup to catch the fresh rainwater. When he drank it, the rest of us sadly thought it would kill him. Miraculously, he began to recover, and soon enough our fevers broke and we were soon back to pursuing our lives in as normal a fashion as possible.

I'd be remiss not to tell a bit more about my cousin "Red John" Dunn's bout with yellow fever. While that cup of cool rainwater may have helped, there was more to his story, as I observed first hand. You must understand that "Red John" was quite the character to behold. He was of a tall lean build, had red hair, and featured a handlebar mustache that you'd have to be blind to miss. It was said that he was so slim that he had to eat breakfast to keep his pants up. "Red John" initially strove to sweat out the disease by lying between two sick cousins that he was caring for. He bashed his head on a table, making it bleed and claiming that the bleeding helped save his life. I'm not thoroughly convinced that the bleeding helped, but "Red John" thought so. Water? Bleeding? Who knows? In any case, he sported a nasty scar from that table-bashing. In truth, bleeding or leeching patients was still a common form of treatment for disease around this time. More about my notorious cousin "Red John" later on.

Causes and treatment of yellow fever remained a mystery, but at least it didn't always end in death. As I said, more about yellow fever and our family later.

FIVE

Love Blossoms

She can ride any horse in my string.

Texas-ism

I realized that at age 27 I wasn't getting any younger. To me, having a home meant having a family – and a big family at that. With the first shots having echoed across the South from Fort Sumter in South Carolina back in 1861, the War Between the States had begun. It was my immediate good fortune to be called upon to supply the Confederacy with cattle and horses. By further good fortune, it meant that I wouldn't have to be in the shooting part of the conflict. I hoped. In any case, little did I know that the Confederate currency I was paid with would soon be worthless. Praise the Lord that I had the foresight to continue my trade with customers other than the Confederacy. Buyers from New Orleans, Louisiana to Abilene, Kansas paid top dollar for my beeves – mostly in relatively reliable Yankee currency and hard coin.

The word we got back from the east was encouraging. President Jefferson Davis was convinced the war wouldn't last long. Newspapers were available but, out here on the Nueces Strip, we often received our news weeks after events had happened.

There were pretty much mixed feelings in Texas. I heard that

German immigrants up in the central part of Texas north of San Antonio were adamantly opposed to secession and made no bones about supporting the Union. It sure made for some stressed relations around Austin. As for me, I tried to stay clear of the politics. I was like most of my fellow South Texas ranchers supporting family members that had donned the butternut gray uniforms of the Confederacy. We needed to produce provisions for our fighting men while keeping an ever-weakening Texas economy alive. From my perspective, I was fighting for lives, not for glory.

Church was an integral part of life my life in Texas. I expect in a sense that it was an extension of our Irish heritage. Normally, Mass was held at my father's house. One Sunday, I was attending Mass in Corpus Christi – and, by the way, we're talking a seriously long ride to church that I might manage to make perhaps once a month – and met a family new to the church. The Corrigans from up near the logically named Corrigan Settlement had brought several children to Mass, but one in particular caught my eye: Andree Ann. Oh, my, but she was a beautiful Irish lass. But, as is my tendency, I'm a bit ahead of my story.

With my fairly decent Irish good looks and a personality honed in the cauldron of trading livestock – humility wasn't in my nature – coupled with a well-muscled physique built from herding livestock and immersion in ranch chores, I wasn't too hard to look at so far as unmarried men in the region were concerned. I did clean up right nice. I expect you might say I was what they called an eligible bachelor. It wasn't a given that all men out here on the Texas frontier would get married. I was quite aware of some nasty stuff going on, as some men chose the solitude of cowboy life and women that didn't find a man occasionally fell to whoring. In the cities, it seemed less likely that either of those eventualities would occur. I'm not entirely sure why that was the case. Perhaps it had to do with societal expectations. In any case, I didn't feature myself choosing solitude. I was very much a social animal, as folks might say.

Having become skilled in negotiating the sales of cattle with

NICHOLAS DUNN-TEXAS LEGEND

complete strangers, I was not a shrinking violet when it came to socializing with people. I had a pretty fair reputation as an honest business man. Despite having only one sister, I wasn't put at any particular disadvantage so far as my understanding of women. In fact, I was used to competing with my seven brothers for just about everything. By my recollection, making Andree Ann's acquaintance went something like the following. She might offer another point of view, but we'll go with mine for now.

I was wearing my Sunday best, which consisted of a dark leather jacket, black trousers, a white – sort of – shirt with pearl buttons, black riding boots featuring silver spurs, and a broad-brimmed white hat that I jauntily cocked ever so slightly to one side. I always rode my best stallion, a big black named Thunder. He'd been birthed during a thunderstorm, and those dark clouds and flashes of lightning seemed to befit his name. I sat a rather fancy black saddle decorated with sterling silver conchos I'd purchased during a trip into Mexico. Altogether, I dressed befitting a reasonably successful rancher during a time of war. But enough of me and my outfit; let's get back to church and Andree Ann.

In keeping with the Dunn family's strong presence in the community, I usually made it a point to sit in a pew near the front of the sanctuary with any of my family who managed to make the journey that particular Sunday. But the front pews offered no seating space this day. I tipped my hat to a couple of my dear cousins, but there simply was no room among my fellow Dunns. I made a quick scan for any other available seats. It was a shade hot, unusually humid, and a bit crowded, and I wound up shedding my jacket and heading to a pew about midway. With many men away fighting for Texas, there were mostly women attending.

As I found a seat, I noticed an absolutely beautiful young lady seated in the pew behind me. Back in Ireland, I'd have described her as *Daithùil* (Da-hoo-il), a true beauty. I reflexively nodded, tipping my hat in my own friendly way. Her demure smile and sparkling blue eyes nearly made me lose my balance as I went to sit down. I half-stumbled and almost sat on my hat. I could swear I heard a giggle from her direction. It was all I could do to not look back over my shoulder. I imagined her mother offering a watch-yourself-cowboy look toward me.

There was always time after Mass to visit with fellow parishioners, and I usually hung around to hear the latest happenings. Today was no exception. The sun was shining, and a soft breeze had begun to waft through the church grounds to take an edge off the heat. I took full advantage of this post-Mass gathering to make my acquaintance with this young lady whose smile so disarmed me.

Her wavy dark locks flowed like silk from beneath her wide-brimmed straw bonnet, and they cascaded down over her graceful ivory neck. Her eyes were made even bluer by the blue in her gingham dress. I quickly caught her eye as she chatted amicably with what apparently were members of her family. She smiled at me. My mind became a jumble of Irish brogue and newly acquired Texas twang, as this *bean álainn* (beautiful woman) put me off balance. I breathed deeply, stood straight, smoothed back my fire-red hair, and strode over to her, hat in hand.

"Pardon, Miss?" I ventured. "I would very much like to make your acquaintance."

"Oh, Mr. Dunn, it's a pleasure to finally meet you."

I was naturally taken aback that she knew who I was. "You know me?"

She smiled that sweet natural smile again. "My daddy purchased some of your beeves a couple of years ago."

I was a bit taken aback. "I see." Hopefully, he had felt fairly treated. "Well, you know my name, Miss. May I have the pleasure of learning yours?"

"Goebel. Andree Ann Goebel, sir." The smile was still gracing her lips. "And you are Nicholas Dunn, famed cattleman, horse breeder, and Comanche fighter of some repute."

"Famed?" I paused, then feigned humbleness. "Perhaps, in these parts." I now recalled her father. He was an honest man to deal with who worked a store and raised a few head of cattle up near what would later become Skidmore. Andree Ann seemed to get her beauty from her mother, and I'll leave it at that. I later learned that her father, Andrew Goebel, had passed away when Andree Ann was an infant, and I had actually dealt with her stepfather, John Corrigan. For a while, the Corrigans had a small settlement named for them near Aransas Creek. Like many settlers of the time, they had their share of Comanche and Lipan Apache attacks and raids by Mexicans.

She introduced me to her mother, Ellen O'Toole Corrigan, and her brothers. Apparently, her stepfather was not able to leave their home that day, owing to some unfinished business. Given the distance, the family had driven a long way. "Would you care to join our picnic, Mr. Dunn?"

That seemed a bit forward at the time, but I deeply appreciated the opportunity to get better acquainted. To make a short story shorter, that day led to a whirlwind courtship inclusive of a few "business" trips to Corrigan Settlement to meet her stepfather about supplies, beeves, and other matters.

I learned of some of the more exciting history of Andree Ann's family. Once when Andree Ann's mother was alone at the family house on Aransas Creek, Indians attacked, killing her dog and stealing her saddle pony. On another occasion, the Indians – likely Karankawas or Lipan Apache – approached but took off when they spotted a stranger up the road preparing his meal by the creek. The man headed to the Corrigan house to find protection. Mrs. Corrigan asked him to ride out and warn her husband who was in the nearby woods cutting timber, but he refused out of his own fear of those savages. Dauntless, she tied a red bandana around her forehead, saddled and mounted a horse, and rode out to warn her husband. When she returned, the Texas Rangers – newly formed – were engaging and chasing off the Indians.

I'd eventually learn that most Indian raids ended tragically. The

Hefferman family had been massacred on Poesta Creek in 1835, and the following year all the horses were stolen from the San Patricio settlement and three folks were killed.

These sorts of clashes continued unabated through 1852, when the Karankawas took a licking at Hines Spring. Thereafter, raids became sporadic, though no less deadly. It's generally acknowledged that we Irish immigrants achieved fame as Indian fighters. You rightly figure that these tales gave me a deep respect for the Indians and kept me always on guard around my ranch and in my speculating travels. You stayed alert, as you could never be certain of what lurked around the next bend in the trail.

During the courtship time with Andree Ann, I set about expanding the main house out on the ranch. It was a measure of the seriousness of my intent. I was going to provide her as much comfort as could be mustered in such untamed country. I put up new clapboard all around, added a big bedroom on the eastern side to catch the rising sun, and built a wide gallery across the full front of the house. I graced it with a couple of rocking chairs my dear Aunt Maggie had seen fit to give me. The gallery offered a spectacular view of the outstretched prairie, with its occasional mottes of live oaks and the bluebonnets, buttercups, winecups, primroses, and all manner of native flowers. I could imagine us sitting under a moonlit sky with the sound of the breeze broken by an occasional owl's hoot or coyote's howl. Indeed, this was God's country, this Texas.

We were married in 1864 in the church in Corpus Christi, where we first met. We were blessed with cessation of the cannonballs the Union Navy situated on the Gulf of Mexico occasionally fired at the city. The sun was shining brightly, a great sign for Irish weddings. I only wish that my grandfather, Long Larry, could have lived to journey from Ireland to attend the wedding. At least, most of my uncles and their families were able to join my own folks and my brothers and sisters, as well as the Corrigans and their family who journeyed down from Victoria.

Andree Ann wore a garland of bluebonnets over her curls that had the effect of intensifying the blue in her eyes. Her smile never left her lips. And they were heavenly lips, to be sure. As was proper in an Irish wedding, a silver Claddagh ring gifted by her mother encircled her ring finger.

Incredibly, by my thinking, someone had the presence of mind to find a couple of bagpipers. To our pleasure, they were decked out in traditional Irish garb from the Balmorals on their heads to their kilts and highland boots. My father seized the occasion to wear his own kilt that he'd brought from Ireland thirteen years earlier and worn upon disembarking to the dock at Corpus Christi. We departed the church to their powerfully melodic sounds.

Everyone gathered at my father's house. Following Irish tradition, a family member, my Uncle Peter, was first to congratulate Andree Ann. This tradition was said to be a guarantee of a great future for the newly wedded couple. The party began. We had no mead, but my father and uncles had managed to gather up what seemed like every bottle of top quality whiskey in Corpus Christi. There was plenty of merriment to be had. I'll never forget the toast my loving father raised:

May there ever be work for your hands to do
May your purse always hold a coin or two
May the sun always shine on your window pane
May a rainbow be certain to follow each rain
May the hand of a friend always be near you
May God fill your heart with gladness to cheer you

After toasts and blessings, I took Andree Ann to the center of the room that served as a dance floor, and led her in our first dance as a married couple. I held her close as we danced and must confess that I longed for much more. As if to torture me, the winsome smile that had drawn me to her at that memorable Mass months before had transformed to one that sent my libido soaring. It would seem like forever until the festivities were ended, and we were climbing into my buckboard for the ride to our home.

Because I strive to be an honorable Christian man, I won't share details of our wedding night. I can vouchsafe that neither of us were disappointed. I do believe we were the happiest, if not the most passionate couple in all of Texas. Might be said that I'd become a legend in her eyes.

We set about to build our lives and make a new Texas family, a destiny if you will. As much in love as we were, it wouldn't take long. Andree Ann loved the house and quickly went about adding what we'd describe as women's touches. I saw some of my own mother in her and felt the comfort that comes with what folks – usually women – often describe as nesting. As I had imagined, we spent many a romantic evening watching the sun set from our gallery. Life was so sweet; it was easy to forget that we lived on a frontier. Wild animals, poisonous snakes, Mexican – and American – bandits, and Indians lurked as real dangers to the unwary. Not many miles to the west, it was far rougher territory.

Andree Ann was more than the love of my life. With family and our neighbors a day or more ride away, ranch life could get pretty lonesome. We had to be self-sufficient, as we didn't have the creature comforts of the sort of civilization found in towns or cities. Andree Ann brought skills to our marriage that were expected of women on the frontier, only she was, in my humble estimation, the very best at them. She could skin and tan the hide of most any critter from deer to coyotes. She'd smoke ham, venison, or beef and occasional buffalo for fine eating later. We didn't have the luxury of store-bought clothes, so her sewing, knitting, and weaving skills were an important contribution. Andree Ann was able to raise several vegetables in a small plot of land I'd fenced off, especially corn. She could make an absolutely awesome cornbread. Let it also be said that, in my humble estimation, Andree Ann could have held her own shooting against the best marksmen on the range. Life on a frontier ranch was very much a partnership.

One morning, as we lolled in bed awaiting the sunrise that signaled our workday, Andree Ann turned to me with a strange smile and ran her finger across my chest. "I missed my bleeding, Nick."

My eyes nearly popped from my head. "You mean?"

"Seems so." Her lips curved up demurely. "Start thinking of names, Mr. Dunn."

This news cemented the reality of our lives together. We truly were going to have our very own family.

Hospitality, especially out in remote areas like our ranch, was a given in Texas. Part of it was our Irish heritage, and part was likely something that ran in the blood of any self-respecting Texan. Guess it could be thought of as a bit contradictory, as a typical Texan on the frontier might be part anti-Mexican Anglo, part puritanical Christian – or faithful Catholics like my family – part adventurer and part southern gentry. Admittedly, the southern gentry part was more likely found in the plantation class among the cotton fields of eastern Texas. Of course, the gentry never did a lick of honest labor. I've been told that, by 1860, there were more than 180,000 Negro slaves, mostly on the plantations of eastern Texas. From what I'd heard from folks passing through, there was ever-increasing fear among Texans that the slaves might eventually rise up in revolt. It's of note that slaves weren't viewed by ranchers as handy tending livestock on vast prairie lands. I can't say as I believed that, and I wouldn't blame that viewpoint as reason why we didn't happen to have any Negro hands on our ranch. So far as I was concerned, the ability to work hard was the only requirement.

In any case, the Mexican *vaqueros* or cowboys were naturals at handling cattle and horses. I did encounter a Negro cowboy or two, and they were every bit as capable and hard-working as any Anglo or Mexican. As to the aforementioned plantation thinking, I'd prefer to believe that our natural Irish hospitality compensated for what we might have lacked in supposed gentrification. As my mother would point out, we didn't have much use for dressed-up dandies whose pants fit too tight. Given the way the British oppressed the Irish people to near-slavery, we harbored a certain appreciation for the injustice of the treatment of the Negros. Despite the indenture system, we weren't chattel, and therein lay the main difference.

One day I headed out, aiming to reach about ten miles west to the far reaches of the ranch, checking on beeves and especially looking for a couple of horses that had gotten loose the previous day. As was our custom, we never went out alone; Carlos, one of my *vaqueros,* rode with me. We figured we'd be back early next day, so didn't even bring a pack horse. A saddle roll was all we needed. Andree Ann packed us some grub consisting of biscuits and dried beef. It was plenty. Oh, and I carried my trusty Colt revolver and brought along my newly acquired .50 caliber Sharps rifle. That Sharps was like shooting a cannon. It wasn't worth much for close-in fighting, but it had deadly effect at a distance. A deer or buffalo hit with a bullet from a Sharps stayed down. For any Comanche in its sights, the result was pretty much the same. Of course, close-in it could double as a club.

We'd ridden several hours and were only a couple of miles from the westernmost ranch boundary when a terrible odor borne along by a warm gentle breeze wafted toward us. It threatened to curl the hair of my goatee. As the stench grew stronger, we reflexively slipped our rifles from their scabbards and wrapped our bandanas over our faces to filter the air. The odor was terrible! Worse than a javelina. Our horses' nostrils flared and they got a bit wild-eyed, so we dismounted, blindfolded the poor cayuses, and walked the dry creek bed. From a cautionary perspective, that likely made sense by way of keeping a low profile. We said nary a word, but Jorge and I were surely experiencing similar thoughts. This sort of situation gets your hackles up, regardless of smells in the air.

We wound our way along the creek bed and followed a wide bend around a motte of live oak. The grisly scene before us sent a cold chill up my spine and stood the hair on the back of my neck straight up. There were half a dozen bodies lying around and beginning to rot in the sun. Flies and other insects swarmed over them. Three of them had been staked out and all manner of horrific torture inflicted. Their deaths were undoubtedly slow and excruciatingly painful. They had been scalped and castrated to say the least. The others apparently had – mercifully – died in the battle. They'd been scalped.

By their dress, the victims met the description of Lipan Apaches. This tribe had been foraging and stealing beeves to trade in Mexico for many years, having taken lessons from their brother Mescalero and Chiricahua Apaches to the west. Lipan Apache, Kiowa, Tonkawa, Comanche, and Karankawa raids had been recorded in South Texas for many years. As I stroked my Sharps rifle, the lingering question for me was who had committed these atrocities that we had just come upon and where were they? Carlos shook his head knowingly as he examined the arrows and the nature of the victims' torture. "*Señor Dunn, estas Comanche.*"

Uncertainty coupled with danger. We were close to the Comancheria I mentioned before. It was said that, if you ran a line up the 98th meridian through Fort Worth, Austin, and San Antonio, any territory west of that line was called Comancheria – Comanche lands. Comancheria was very definitely a place you did not want to be if you hoped to keep your hair.

The Comancheria was shrinking bit by bit with the encroachment of Anglo settlers, but that merely squeezed the Comanche enough to make them ever more desperate and more dangerous. This had been borne out a few years earlier when, as I previously described, a large band of 1,000 or so Penateka Comanche led by Buffalo Hump swept through South Texas. Despite being chased down for weeks by Texas Rangers during their retreat, the Comanche escaped with most of the stolen horses and other loot. That was made all the more frustrating in that they traveled slowly with women and children hauling their worldly goods along on the ubiquitous travois. The fact that most Comanche escaped long served as an embarrassment.

But back to my present concern. While these Comanche had no doubt left the area, given that the bodies had lain in the dry creek bed for at least a couple of days, we decided it would be best to head back to the relative safety of the ranch. The Comanche had wandered well beyond their normal hunting grounds. With only the two of us, it would have been foolhardy to hang around.

We rode all night, arriving at the ranch compound at just about sunup, with no rounded-up longhorns or horses, but very much alive. It was eye-opening on the one hand and memorable if for no other reason than that horrendous stench and seeing what angry Comanche did to their victims.

Andree Ann was standing on the porch to greet us. A pregnant woman's hands-on-hips stance demanded a straight answer to the obvious question, "Why are you back so soon?"

What could I say but the truth? "Wouldn't have been a good idea to stay out there, love." Then I lowered the hammer so to speak, "It seemed that some Apaches fell victim to Comanche warriors."

Andree Ann's face paled. She clearly recognized the gravity. This was far too close. This made it very easy to justify having a couple of loaded rifles mounted in strategic spots around the house and outbuildings. "Thank God, you're safe." She hugged me tightly. I could feel her growing belly, and it made me feel all the more concerned for our safety and well-being.

"I think they're all getting desperate." Andree Ann and I had talked previously about how the extension of the frontier was starting to squeeze the Indian territories. "We have to be on guard."

I'd been told that the Comanche had been contained pretty far north and west of our ranch beyond what some were calling the Balcones Escarpment. A Texas Ranger named John "Rip" Ford had mounted a very effective campaign against the Comanche back in the late 1850s up in north Texas on the Canadian River. He managed to push them westward, and some savages were housed at Camp Cooper on the Brazos River. Many were supposedly being moved to lands in Oklahoma Territory just north of the Red River, but there were no guarantees they'd stay there. In fact, to my knowledge, Buffalo Hump came and went as suited his druthers. 'Course I hadn't been up in that part of Texas since my droving days. And droving cattle had changed, mostly thanks to economics. Lord knows, with the fencing that accompanied the farms and plantations plus our more convenient nearby access to Corpus Christi, droving to Abilene and parts north was left to more well-resourced folks like Charles Goodnight. Better for us to drove our cattle to Corpus.

"I wonder whether the army knows?" Andree Ann was, of course, referring to the Confederate Army stationed near what would later become Robstown along the route to Corpus Christi. They were patrolling the length of the Nueces Strip and were few in number, so it was likely we'd find them more by chance. They had essentially replaced the Texas Rangers, who had ceased to be official as far as full government authorization. The few men that had served were being used to support troops. If a soldier or two happened through nearby Nuecestown, all the better. I'll talk more to it later, but it's important to understand that the Texas Rangers weren't even authorized during the War Between the States, so essentially didn't really exist. We had to rely on Confederate Army and Cavalry along with local sheriffs.

I pondered a moment on whether the Confederate Army ought to be concerned about the Comanche. "I'm thinking it makes sense to let the soldiers know. I'll send one of our hands up to Robstown." I knew that was likely a fool's errand given the vast territory the soldiers were covering. It seemed to reassure Andree Ann a bit, though it did nothing to ease my own concerns. Also, Andree Ann was already quite well along with child, and the protective juices that come with parenthood were flowing within me. I would soon have a family to protect. The vast expanse of the Comancheria wasn't that far away.

There was a lot to be concerned about out there. With the Texas

Rangers mostly absent and the Confederate Army distracted, we were just a tad vulnerable, to put it mildly. Mexican banditos as well as revolutionaries occasionally ventured north of the border to "forage," and the U.S. Cavalry was more intent on stopping Confederate cotton and weapons trading than chasing Indians. For folks like us Dunns and other frontier settlers, we were pretty much on our own. Moreover, we had already heard about some yellow fever cases breaking out in Corpus Christi.

Andree Ann broke my line of thought. "Sweetheart, come on in, and I'll cook you some breakfast." The chickens scattered and a couple of pigs grunted, as if on cue. Eggs and bacon sounded great.

SIX

War Finally Touches Us

Tough? He'd fight a rattlesnake and spot him the first bite.

Texas-ism

My father, John Dunn, Sr., had been prospering on his roughly 170-acre ranch. In addition to growing cotton, he had a dozen horses, about 150 beeves, and 75 sheep. He was successful enough by 1861 to purchase another 110 acres the following year. By then, the Dunn family had managed to acquire several thousands of acres across the Nueces Strip in South Texas. It could be said that the entire family was prospering, but the uncertainties of war were looming on our horizon.

Keep in mind that Andree Ann and I had married in the midst of what became known as the War Between the States. The northerners, or Yankees, called it the Civil War. Wasn't anything civil about it. So, there I was, trying to start a family in the midst of upheaval, yet actually was isolated from the worst of it by virtue of the frontier location of our ranch. We feared foraging expeditions from both Rebel and Yankee troops, but blessedly they never materialized. I can't say I was sure as to how I might react to military predations of any kind from either side.

It's estimated that roughly 70,000 Texans eventually served in the

Confederate Army. That was roughly a third of the male population of the state at the time. I did try to stay abreast of the political goings-on. I heard that Governor Sam Houston had accepted the vote on Texas secession from the Union but refused to take the oath of allegiance to the Confederacy. He was deposed from office March 16, 1861. It was a shame, as on whole Sam Houston was a truly great Texan. It wasn't widely known, but Houston had once held dreams of annexing Mexico and becoming president of the United States. With his ouster, Lieutenant Governor Clark assumed the governorship and then ran for governor that fall but lost in a close election fraught with allegations of fraud. He was replaced by the election winner, Francis Lubbock. Notably, Lubbock supported conscription of all able-bodied men, including resident aliens. I can't say as I was very fond of conscription and was grateful not to be called, apparently due to the value placed on my ranch to supply beeves for the Confederate Army. I suppose it could be said that I served in a different way. As I will share later, our family did suffer losses in service to the Confederacy. I wasn't surprised to later learn that Governor Lubbock, his successor Pendleton Murrah, and fellow secessionists fled to Mexico after the war. I had a nagging feeling that they weren't the most honest of men.

In separating from the Union, I observed that most of what Yankees called the Deep South worked to support a sort of patriarchal republic as it had existed through the antebellum period. White males stood atop the social order, with plantation-owning slaveholders possessing a higher status than white men who owned no slaves. Secession actually represented a contradiction of sorts in preservation of a political structure while rebelling to maintain the established order. The southern aristocracy sought to get rid of the political corruption of the North while protecting their slave-based agrarian economy. Accomplishing this entailed reconciling slave owners with the majority of folks who owned no slaves.

It sounds over-simplified but, like it or not, slavery was at the core of the crisis within the Union. States' rights were part of the political mix, but slavery became the focal point. Had not Texas been viewed politically and geographically as part of the South, we might not have seceded. Slavery was not so prevalent in my part of Texas, although it was rampant throughout those eastern counties. I, for one, appreciated a hard-working free Negro cowboy as much as any drover on a drive. Shoot, if Texas were to secede, we ought to be an independent republic again, rather than be a part of a confederacy of states that didn't share most of our values.

Admittedly, I was more concerned with my livestock business than worrying about the politics that led to what would turn out to be a devastating conflict of arms. From what I heard, President Lincoln was determined to hold the Union together by military force despite the fact that the Constitution did not forbid states to secede. Lincoln apparently suspended what they called *habeas corpus* so he could jail opponents to his policies without the Constitutional benefit of a trial. It certainly marked a dark period in our history so far as I was concerned. It led to a devastating loss of military and civilian lives, disruption of the economy, extra burdens on women and children, and breakdown of transportation and communications systems. On a somewhat lighter note, the supply of coffee to the troops was severely disrupted. Resourceful soldiers tried brewing okra, barley, corn, and peanuts to no avail. As any self-respecting Texan knows, there really is no substitute for coffee.

It was late in the afternoon. Andree Ann's time had come. She was going into labor. There was no time to fetch my mother, so I relied on my *vaquero* Carlos' wife to help Andree Ann through labor.

For what seemed an eternity, I nervously sat on the stoop of the gallery waiting for news. Was it always to be like this? At last, the silence was broken by a plaintive cry. Ellender "Nellie" Dunn had come forth into the world, and she made certain that the whole world knew it. She was full-throated enough that I could even hear Thunder's startled whinny over in the stable.

I hesitated and then went to Andree Ann's side. She was tired but gave me the most incredibly joyful smile. Nellie nestled in her arms. "You've got yourself a beautiful daughter, Nicholas Dunn." And she handed her up to me.

Now, I had helped birth beeves, horses, and all manner of critters, but none of that came close to holding my own child. I looked down at Andree Ann. "You are so beautiful." I recollect a bit of a tear in the corner of my eye. My, but it was a happy moment. Nellie seemed so fragile in my strong cowboy arms and ranch-toughened hands. Fearful of dropping her, I lay baby Nellie back in Andree Ann's loving motherly arms.

At that, I went out on the gallery, took off my hat, and hollered the biggest holler that was ever heard south of Austin. We had a family! My breeder bull Bert bellowed in accompaniment.

From this point forward, my life was changed – I think for the better. As a businessman, my view of life had been about the "game" of buying and selling beeves, to amass land and wealth for its own sake. As a family man, my view was vastly broadened, as buying and selling beeves became deadly serious toward providing sustenance for my growing family. It was no longer a game. It also gave me a new perspective on the lives of my grandfather Long Larry Dunn and my father John. Long Larry certainly would have been proud.

I didn't realize just how fully my life had changed and how my priorities had shifted until a few weeks later. It had gotten warm, and we hadn't seen rain for a while. The prairie was bone dry, and it was all our livestock could do to find water.

Now, there are times when you sense that something unwelcome was near at hand. You could sort of feel it in the air. This was one of those times. Your instincts come alive, slapping you up the side of your head with a big dose of uncertainty. Off in the distance, I could see thunderheads building. Rain would bring welcome relief, and I could readily imagine our cisterns being refilled with the cloud's bounty. Today, I found myself especially concerned with an unusually strong breeze sweeping across our land in front of the gathering storm. I watched for a few minutes from the corral gate, eyeing the approaching storm while keeping an eye on our prize bull, Bert. I headed to the ranch house as the thunderheads continued to well up to an enormous size. The storm could bring flash flooding and, just as bad, fire.

"Andree Ann! Andree Ann!" I leaped to the galley and dashed into the house.

"What is it, Nick?"

"There's a big storm brewing. Grab Nellie and get into the cellar." I'd had the presence of mind to build a sort of secret space under the house where my family could hide in an emergency. Safety took precedence over a few nasty spiders.

Andree Ann snatched up baby Nellie and hustled into the cellar.

"I'll be back in a bit." And I went back outside. All manner of brush and dust were beginning to kick up. Then, my worst fears were realized. The clouds weren't delivering rain. Soon enough, bolts of lightning sent their fiery shards into the bone-dry prairie grass just north of our ranch. With that, I saw the first signs of fire as wisps of smoke rose in the distance. Fed by the strong shifting winds, fire could get out of control fast.

There wasn't much anyone could do about prairie fires. We weren't able to build firebreaks and, even if we did, it's unlikely a fire like the one that was brewing would be stopped by anything we mere humans could place in its path. It was a helpless feeling. I hoped and prayed that it would spare us and, more important, spare our livestock out on the open range. There was no way I could mount and gather my longhorns and horses fast enough. Assuming the fire passed us by, I resigned myself to eventually going out and putting suffering beasts out of their misery.

There's something almost prehistoric about fire. Perhaps it's the knowledge that fire has been around as long as humans and likely earlier. I was taught that it is important toward regenerating the landscape, killing off the deep-rooted mesquite and cedar trees and allowing the prairie grasses our livestock rely on to come back and truly flourish. Of course, the hearty mesquite and live oak would come back soon enough to afford savannahs with shady mottes as refuge from the broiling sun. It was a price that was exacted on the frontier.

I figured that the fire I saw coming at us from the distance was likely not the only one in the region. I prayed that lives would be spared. Meanwhile, I did what I could to use what water we had to throw wet cloths up on the roof of our house to protect it as far as our limited means allowed. I thought about letting Bert and the saddle horses out of the corrals but decided they might panic and run in the wrong direction.

Just as the monster of a fire was a couple of hundred yards away from engulfing our home, it began to rain...a good hard gully-washer of a rain. Such a blessing! I strained to hear the sizzle and hiss of flames being extinguished. Dear God, it was a great sound.

I checked Bert and the horses. Bert actually had a few charred pieces of prairie grass on his broad back. The big bull welcomed the rain, too.

The thunderheads moved off toward the east and took the rain and lightning with them. I called Andree Ann out of the house to share in our good fortune. We took a walk arm in arm around the house and outbuildings. I stomped out a few smoldering embers just north of the barn. It amazed me that any fire had survived the rain.

We looked at each other. She knew what I had to do, and soon enough I'd saddled Thunder and headed out to see how our livestock had fared.

We were about as lucky as could be expected. Most longhorns and horses had successfully fled far enough to avoid the monster fire's wrath. I did have to put down four cows, a calf, and two horses that had suffered burns or injured themselves trying to escape. I surely hated to have to destroy such noble beasts.

Saints be praised, my family was most important, and we were unscathed. Then, I noticed a couple of burn spots on the shoulder of my shirt.

I learned that a couple of neighbors hadn't fared so well. A couple of folks suffocated to death by smoke and others lost buildings and livestock. It sure increased our sense of community as we reached out to help unfortunate neighbors as best we could. It was simply what we did.

Next day, my father stopped by. The fire had bypassed his spread along with the fields of cotton. Nothing living had been lost. We all prayed that we would never see another prairie fire, though we knew of the very real possibility.

I've referred several times to the War Between the States, so please allow me to share a bit more about the war years that did impact us.

Early in the War Between the States, Corpus Christi served as a vital crossroads for Confederate commerce. Little wonder that it became a target of Union forces. The Yankees blockaded the port of Corpus Christi beginning in 1862. They occasionally bombarded the town. They were at least considerate enough to give advance warning of their bombardments, so women and children could be evacuated. An excerpt from an article in a weekly publication called "The Rancher" best illustrates the situation, as it describes the entry of Yankee gunboats under the command of Lieutenant Commander J.W. Kittredge to Corpus Christi Bay:

> *"Next morning, the commander of the Yankees landed at the*
> *upper wharf, under a flag of truce, and was met by Major*
> *A.M. Hobby, commander of this post. A parley was held, but*
> *no definite results obtained. At 4 p.m., same day, by*

agreement, the same parties again met, when the Yankee

captain demanded the right and claimed it as a prerogative

to inspect the buildings of this place under the ensign of the

U.S. Major Hobby promptly refused his demands, denied his

claims, and informed the Yankee that whenever he landed on

our soil he would be attacked. An armistice of 48 hours was

arranged...every family moved to the country...then the

defenders fired first...the bombardment was day long...

nobody hurt, not much damage. Sunday, the fleet used for

repair. Monday morning bombardment started again.

About 10 a.m., 32 Marines landed on the beach with a six-

pound field piece. Twenty-five men left the defense battery

and chased the Marines away. Four Marines were killed or

wounded; the defenders had one killed, one wounded. The

bombardment resumed for the rest of the day, then the fleet

withdrew...over 400 shells did much damage to the city."

The Yankees occupied the town toward the end of 1863, and they created considerable inconvenience for us by virtue of their presence. I hear tell that Kittredge had a habit of coming ashore to satisfy his taste for buttermilk. He went ashore once too often. The Yankee was captured by a Confederate patrol, sent to San Antonio, and eventually paroled. Enterprising traders turned to using small, shallow-draft boats to avoid the blockade and transport goods along a route inside the barrier islands. I suppose we should have been grateful that the Union Army didn't practice the "scorched-earth" tactics they were said to use, especially General Sherman's march to the sea in which he destroyed Atlanta and Charleston and conducted the widespread burning of towns and farms in the Blue Ridge Valley of Virginia. Those tactics would do the job of breaking the economic and emotional back of much of the South, and it would take decades to recover. I learned years later that the Union Army had pretty much regularly violated some new rules of warfare called the *Geneva Convention*. Doggone Yankees!

I was grateful that my family was spared Sherman's tactics. Praise God on that count. It was tough enough carving out a living on the frontier. As I've said earlier, it had little or no impact on my wedding to Andree Ann.

A little-known feature that was unknown to the Yankees and handy for those looking to quickly transport goods between San Patricio and Corpus Christi was Reef Road. It was comprised of beds of oyster shells that divided Corpus Christi Bay and Nueces Bay. At low tide, it enabled early settlers and Indians to cross the expanse in a mere 18 to 24 inches of water. Of course, it wasn't a straight line, so you had to know its course. Reef Road was apparently discovered by settlers after an Indian attack on a settlement in Nueces County. It was said that Texas Rangers chased them to the water's edge. Figuring that the Indians were surrounded by water and wouldn't be going anywhere, the Rangers camped for the night. Next morning, they found footsteps leading into the water. The Indians had made their escape crossing via the reef. Anyway, Reef Road saved many a traveler around 50 miles, or a couple of days on horseback. People even used it instead of the ferries and the later railroads with their bridges.

For a while, the War Between the States didn't really touch us but, by 1863, it inevitably hit us in a bigger way than we might have imagined. My father had been raising cotton on part of his ranch. He raised a lot of it and – as I mentioned – given how labor-intensive growing cotton was, he had a few Negro slaves. I'd say that slavery or the attitude toward that institution was different in our part of Texas than other parts of the Confederacy. The vast expanse of South Texas, coupled with an economy that mostly didn't depend on slave labor, gave the black folk more opportunity.

As I hear tell, many free Negroes and former slaves in Texas married into Spanish families and had become fairly wealthy. By contrast, the aristocratic elite of the Deep South and even eastern Texas lived in what was best called a highly paternalistic society that rested on an air of white male superiority. Slaves were denied education and intellectual improvement, partly because those things were inappropriate to their situation but also because it minimized any threat of insurrection. Yet slaves were mostly cared for in sickness, housed and fed, and made as comfortable as necessary to protect them as an investment. From what I was able to observe, my father treated slaves pretty well. Perhaps it was by our own family experience of being socially and economically enslaved in Ireland by the English. I found myself partial to that British fellow, William Wilberforce, a member of Parliament who led the ending of the British slave trade by passage of the Slave Trade Act of 1807. My father held him in high regard and made certain we knew of him.

My father sent his cotton southward to Matamoros, Mexico by wagon train with 16 to 18 horses or a couple teams of oxen hitched to each wagon. It was an impressive sight to see those wagons near bursting with bales of cotton on what was referred to as the Cotton Road. The route was located about 40 miles inland from the Gulf. It took about three weeks to make the 330-mile round trip over very poor territory. Of course, Matt, Patrick, Mike, and Christopher joined me in guarding the wagon train, as there were banditos, Yankee troops, and even occasional hostile Comanche and Apache to deal with. We generally took along about a dozen armed outriders as escorts. The Comanche and Apache especially coveted good horse stock, but it was the Union Cavalry that had us most concerned. As a matter of fact, special care had to be taken near Brownsville, as the town changed hands between Confederates and Yankees at least five times that I recall. We usually gave the city a wide berth.

I likely as not contributed to my reputation as an Indian fighter on one of these trips. We were attacked by a couple of dozen Lipan Apache. As I recall, it went pretty much as follows.

We first spotted the Apache war party on a rise a good distance off. As Apache guns started sending bullets at us, Matt called out, "Nick! Nick! Apache!" The savages were a tad over-anxious, as their bullets couldn't yet reach us. Figures Matt would call on me, as tales had spread about my exploits fighting Comanche as a drover guiding cattle north to Missouri and Kansas. It should be noted that Comanche and Apache used different tactics. The Comanche aimed to draw you into a diversionary ambush before they stole your horses, while the Apache sought to overwhelm by brute savage force. Apache were generally regarded as not so devious as Comanche. Besides, they were interested in the beeves, not the horses.

I actually stayed pretty calm, as the savages were out of range and lousy marksmen, especially from horseback. Again, the difference between Comanche and Apache stood in stark contrast, as the Comanche were far superior horsemen who could shoot arrows with fairly good accuracy at a gallop. Knowing these differences, I wheeled around on the roan I was riding and charged headlong at the Apache with my rifle and Colt spewing lead. They were certainly not expecting a lone rider to be so bold. "Mike, Matt, come on!" My brothers promptly joined the charge.

I shot three Apache from their ponies and, by the time Mike and Matt joined in the skirmish, the savages were in full flight. I recall that we got at least one more, likely shot by one of my brothers.

I expect that, between this sort of Indian fighting and my experience against Comanche as a drover, it earned me that Indian fighter appellation. It certainly raised my stock with my family and our neighbors. Whether it qualified as legendary or not is a matter of personal perspective.

We continued to endure the trading runs on the Cotton Road. Please keep in mind that cotton was big business in the South, and the

Yankee blockade of southern ports was highly effective. You might say the "white gold" was the economic backbone of the Confederacy. To finance the Confederate war effort, cotton was run from Texas across the Rio Grande through Matamoros and deep into Mexico to Vera Cruz for export, mostly to Europe. Alternatively, the Rio Grande served as a sort of grand waterway that the Yankee navy could not effectively blockade, such that steamboats could slip past patrols and haul the cotton upriver. Thus, the South's "white gold" could be traded for weapons and supplies for the Confederacy. I must add that my father returned with gun powder, rifles, military supplies, medicine, food, dress goods, lead, and percussion caps after delivering our cotton cargo.

Tragically, my Uncle Thomas, one of my father's brothers, died as a result of one of our journeys down the Cotton Road. He'd just returned from a trip down the road in 1863. He was tired, drenched with rain, and possibly suffering from dysentery. He developed a high fever and passed away.

The war continued and, by my humble estimation, the conflict was not going well for the Confederacy.

On August 20, 1864, the War Between the States touched our family in a far more sorrowful way than any of us might have expected. My brother Lawrence was home on furlough with a broken arm caused by a rifle ball received during a bombardment of and attack upon Corpus Christi. He had enlisted as a private with the 1st Regiment, Texas Cavalry, 1st Mounted Rifles under Lieutenant Colonel William Yager in 1862. As I understand it, Lawrence spent some time early in his service stationed in a garrison up at Niblett's Bluff guarding an important border crossing between Louisiana and Texas. In Louisiana, Colonel Yager's command had been directly involved in repelling the advances of Union Major General Banks on three occasions despite being vastly outnumbered. Excuse my satisfied smile as I recall what must have been quite embarrassing to General Banks.

I believe my brother was later sent south to Camp Aransas where his unit engaged Federal foraging parties along the coast. Yager's command was under Brigadier General Henry McCullough, previously of Texas Ranger fame, and Yager was noted for no-nonsense discipline and great training in saber and general cavalry battle tactics. Having many recruits from the Texas Rangers, the Texas Cavalry in general was famous for its highly effective use of the weapons at its disposal, mostly light artillery, rifles, shotguns, pistols, and sabers. Yager's command was charged with ensuring resupply of Confederate forces and fending off inland forays by Union troops. Following successes at Aransas, Yager's cavalry was sent to the Ringgold Barracks near Brownsville. His unit – and I believe Lawrence was among them – experienced dazzling successes against the Yankees, even carrying out a brazen daylight raid that resulted in beaching a Yankee merchantman on the Gulf of Mexico filled with its cargo of valuable goods.

While home recuperating from his injury, Lawrence volunteered to accompany a Captain James Ware of the 1st Regiment of Texas Cavalry and ten men to Padre Island southeast of Corpus Christi to capture a gang of Mexican cattle thieves and accompanying white traitors who were butchering Texas beeves and selling the hides and even some of the meat to the Yankees. They called these despicable characters hiders. Like most of our family, Lawrence could speak Spanish fluently. He also knew the island quite well. I never got to see Lawrence in his uniform but, knowing his style and from the few times we observed other units near the ranch, I imagine him clothed in the durable butternut-colored gray standard-issue uniform with a checked shirt, dark brown boots, heavy spurs, wide-brimmed hat, bandana round his neck, and a canteen. He was always well-armed. He carried his .44 caliber Colt Walker revolver, plus a Confederate-issue Remington revolver, short double-barreled shotgun, saber, a large Bowie knife, and possibly a pair of English Enfield rifles. He had the appropriate assortment of ammunition as required.

When the party saw the thieves – rustlers, if you will – they found them well entrenched in the sand hills and noted that there were about 40 of them. They were busy killing beeves and stripping the hides. Captain Ware had the men dismount, and then called for a volunteer to go under a flag of truce and ask them to surrender. For a moment, the men stood looking furtively at one another. Since he could parlay in Spanish, Lawrence volunteered. He mounted, tied a white handkerchief to the muzzle of his rifle, wiped a few beads of sweat from his face and neck with his bandana, and rode over to the thieves' encampment. I'm sure he looked quite official in his Confederate uniform. I heard later that the brief parlay went something like this.

Three of the rustlers broke away from the encampment and rode out to meet Lawrence. They were as rough a looking trio as could ever be conjured up. They were well-armed and acted none too pleasant. Two of the Mexicans had bandoliers draped across their chests. They wore large broad-brimmed hats typical of the style of their people.

Lawrence confirmed that the thieves outnumbered Captain Ware's force, but the cavalry unit was much better-armed. *"Vaqueros! Por favor. Entreguen sus armas!"* Lawrence stood ramrod straight in the saddle as he asked them to surrender their arms. Lawrence could present an imposing figure, despite his arm still being in a sling. I never learned details about his experiences in the War, but I'm sure he must have been among the braver soldiers in the battles. We did harken back to a long line of Irish chieftains and warriors known for their ferocious, fanatical bravery.

The apparent leader of the rustlers threw his head back with a nasty laugh and snarled, *"Americano! Es chiste!"* He told Lawrence that he must be joking.

Lawrence insisted more forcefully, *"Entreguen sus armas!"* Then, he added, *"Si te rindes, eres libre de salir pacíficamente."* He offered them the chance to leave peacefully.

"Los Americanos estas locos!" The Mexican laughed again, the laugh punctuated with a squinty-eyed, self-satisfied smirk. He likely

already observed that his force outnumbered the Confederates as they stood beside their horses on a sand dune a hundred yards or so behind Lawrence.

Lawrence gave the man a don't-mess-with-us look and turned his horse to return to the Confederate line. At that, the Mexican thieves opened fire, and Lawrence was hit several times in the back, although he managed to stay in the saddle. My brother Matt and five other soldiers mounted and galloped out to meet him. They helped him from his well-lathered horse. Captain Ware dismounted out of respect as my brother Matt cradled Lawrence's head off the ground. Matt later told me that Lawrence spoke only a single sentence before breathing his last, "Had bad luck." He was only 27 years old. With Lawrence's death, Captain Ware sprung to his saddle, and the company charged full bore, routing the Mexicans. From what I heard, they didn't spare a single one of those Mexican thieves.

My father was devastated, as any parent who loses a child would be. It was the first time we had lost a member of our immediate family to violence. It would turn out to not be the last.

In any case, we all felt holes in our hearts over the loss of Lawrence. I have to admit that the hole I felt might have been a bit larger owing to guilt I felt over possibly contributing to the Mexican's actions. It seems that a short time before the incident, I had severely reprimanded a Mexican who had mixed one of my horses with some that he was driving through town, threatening to have the man arrested. I occasionally would unbridle my temper, and that was rarely a good thing. Apparently, that created a strong grudge by some Mexicans against me and likely anyone named Dunn. Still, it just didn't seem right that God should take such a fine young man as my brother.

By this time, we were following the War Between the States mostly through newspaper accounts and stories from folks who occasionally passed through. It finally came to an inglorious end. I can't say that

any of us were surprised. It was well known that many had died –
some say as many as 600,000 – on both sides and still more bore
physical and mental wounds. Notably and pretty much lost in history
is the fact that one of the last battles of the War was fought just south
of Brownsville near the Rio Grande. It was memorable for me if for
no other reason than we used to skirt around Brownsville when we
delivered cotton to Matamoros.

On May 13, 1865, just a month after General Robert E. Lee's
surrender at Appomattox, a Confederate force under Colonel John
"Rip" Ford captured 800 Yankee soldiers. The Battle of Palmito
Ranch turned out to be the final victory for the Confederacy. It's been
reported that the last soldier from either side killed in battle happened
at the Battle of Palmito Ranch. I suppose losing the war was a bitter
pill for some to swallow, and those troops at Palmito Ranch surely
had to put up a last stand of sorts. This win served to essentially be
just another symbol of the fruitlessness of the Confederate cause.
Still, Texans weren't used to losing. I did hear tell of a sort of ironic
happening, when Union General Lew Wallace met with a couple of
Confederate generals in Texas to negotiate an early accord that would
have hastened our re-admittance to the Union. Some half-cocked
Confederate general named John G. Walker reportedly got full of
himself and put a lid on any deal, thus extending the war until the
Palmito Ranch encounter. I expect I shouldn't be too tough on General
Walker, as he had apparently performed valiantly for General Lee
back east and had distinguished himself leading what was called the
Greyhound Division that repeatedly stopped Yankee invasions from
Louisiana into Texas.

I heard about a month later, June 19 to be exact, an announcement
was delivered in Houston that officially freed the slaves. It's an
understatement to say that it didn't take anyone by surprise.

Word filtered back as to the dark side of war. I heard about soldier
and animal corpses rotting in the sun for days after battles, of piles of
amputated limbs outside field hospitals, of disease-racked soldiers, and

of man's general inhumanity to man. It harkened back to recollections of my Uncle Matt's experiences in the Mexican-American War. I also heard another side of this macabre business of war, as surgeons strove to save lives and volunteer nurses soothed the dying and wounded. Again, I felt so blessed to have missed the horrors of battle. I understand that being captured was likened to a death sentence, as disease and pestilence wracked the prisoner populations.

One of the nastiest parts of the Yankee victory was the sense of entitlement and condescension that characterized the occupying troops. Reconstruction was a bitter pill to swallow. The more unsavory characters among those charged with implementing reconstruction were hard over on punishing "Johnny Rebs," as they often called us white folk. Carpetbaggers descended like a plague of locusts. Typical was an incident with occupying soldiers in late 1866 that my brother Matt shared with us.

One Sunday morning, two Negroes of a Negro company of soldiers – they were called "buffalo soldiers" – stationed in Corpus Christi after the War deserted, got drunk, and decided to make trouble. They entered Matt's house while he was off with the family attending Mass in town. The Negroes dressed themselves in some of his clothes, stole his pistols and a couple of horses, and left the house. They were gone when Matt and his family returned from church later that evening to discover the guns and the Union army uniforms they had left behind. They had been none too careful, and that led Matt to figure that they were probably drunk having gotten their confidence up with demon liquor.

The next morning, Matt rode to the encampment to see the commanding officer and report the incident. He rode calm and determined through the camp gate, dismounted, and tied his horse at the hitching post in front of the commanding officer's tent.

The Negro guard let the captain know Matt was there to see him about an important matter.

The officer, the only white man in the Company, staggered groggily from the tent, squinted, and surveyed my brother Matt from boot tips to hat crown.

"Good morning, Captain. My name is Matthew Dunn, and it appears that a few of your Negroes took liberties with my property yesterday while I was at church." Matt was holding his temper, trying to be as respectful as possible in reference to the thieves.

The captain dismissed Matt's accusation. "My soldiers were accounted for all day yesterday. I suggest you be on your way, Mr. Dunn."

"Captain, I do urge you to please check your roster. I would like to recover my horses and belongings." He was chewing on the unsaid fact that horse thieves in Texas were generally hung.

The officer grunted, "Can't help you," turned silently, and went back inside his tent.

Matt was pretty angry, but he kept his peace. Matt likely as not stroked the hammer of his holstered revolver and was half-tempted to use it.

Next morning, Matt observed the camp at the roll call and noticed two names were not answered. He called this to the officer's attention, but the captain again denied that his men were guilty. He told Matt to get the deserters himself – if they were in fact deserters – and not to come bothering him.

Matt silently mounted his horse and rode out of the encampment. He had a vague idea where he might find the thieves, as it was pretty common those days for miscreants to head for the shores of Nueces Bay where there were plenty of places to hide.

Sure enough, Matt found the deserters on a peninsula along Nueces Bay. He ordered them to surrender, but instead they started shooting at him. Those drunken Negroes picked the wrong man to shoot at. Like most Dunns, Matt was a crack shot with rifle or pistol. It was a necessary skill out on the range where all manner of nasty critters might lurk. Anyway, Matt opened fire on them, killing one almost immediately and roping the other after the half-sotted deserter's pistol jammed. Matt gathered the belongings they'd stolen, threw the dead Negro over the back of his pack horse, and sat the other on one of the stolen horses with his hands tied behind his back and a rope around his neck. The one on the horse must have been a pretty picture, still drunk and now stripped down to his underwear. Matt drove him ahead to the encampment, where he delivered him and his dead comrade to the commanding officer.

The guard saw Matt coming and alerted the officer inside the tent. The captain emerged quickly and watched silently as Matt guided the thief toward him. Matt had forced his hand.

Matt tipped his hat in a gentlemanly way. "Captain, I think I found something you lost. I'm sorry about the one over there, but they tried to shoot me with my own pistols. Can you believe that?" Matt smiled an ironic sort of smile that was unique to him. "I have my pistols and stolen horses back, so I'll leave this Negro with you to deal with."

"Er, thank you, Mr. Dunn. Sorry to have troubled you."

By now, the two Negroes had been pulled off Matt's horses, so he grabbed their lead lines, turned, and headed back to his ranch. I wish I'd been there to see the expression on that captain's face.

As to how I felt about all this? Like most Texans, we were a prideful and stubborn race and that was compounded in us hardheaded Irishmen. We had quite a legacy. Our Anglo forefathers in America had whipped the British twice, kicked Mexican army butts twice, and put a whipping on most all the Indian tribes in Texas. It served to make the coming nine years of post-war humiliations at the hands of the Union military next to unbearable.

So there continued to be ill feelings for some time. It's my understanding that many Negroes in the south took out years of their frustrations of enslavement by attacking white folks without provocation. There were many nasty incidents of beatings, robberies, and even murders that those charged with law enforcement were none too inclined to do much about. The Texas Rangers had been officially disbanded and the Reconstructionist governor had the temerity – at the time – to recruit many Negroes to the police force. While I never encountered an issue with Negro police officers, I was told that they often as not would get carried away in handing out their peculiar brand of justice tinged with vengeance. However, they just as often would be on the receiving end of vigilante justice. I'm not complaining, mind you, as the Texas Rangers had also delivered a nasty form of frontier law, not to mention those seemingly ever-present emotionally charged vigilance committees that would organize as needed to right perceived wrongs.

Andree Ann and I did our level best to maintain family normalcy while paying attention to news reports about the post-war reconstruction. Being way over near the Collins settlement, we hadn't had so much direct contact with the war other than furnishing beef to troops and having occasionally helped my father transport cotton. The year before we were wed, we had learned about the terrible losses at Gettysburg. It was hard to imagine the horror of so many lives lost, families ripped apart, and human beings maimed for life. I prayed the country would never experience such horrors again.

While I'm not proud of it in retrospect, Andree Ann and I had briefly kept a couple of household slaves. George and Clara were pretty much treated like family, but the fact remained that they were not free. As I've mentioned, my father also owned a few slaves to help with the cotton crop. We were already aware that the British had outlawed the slave trade, thanks to some fellow named William Wilberforce back in the early 1900s, but my adopted country – especially the South – was very much economically dependent on slave labor. President Lincoln had issued the Emancipation Proclamation, but that didn't impact us in Texas right away. Anyway, George and Clara helped Andree Ann around the house. We focused our efforts mostly on carving out a life here in Texas regardless of politics and the like. After the War, George and Clara stayed on though they were now employed as laborers, receiving room and board in exchange for their efforts. They were free to earn money as they could.

Reconstruction was a mixed bag for Andree Ann and me. Having sold a lot of cattle in exchange for worthless Confederate currency, it took much effort to recover financially. The speed of that recovery was affected somewhat by the slowed economic rebound of the South in general. Blessedly, Corpus Christi bounced back fairly quickly. My skills as a livestock speculator were tested. Importantly, the trails to the northern railheads reopened and soon enough there would be slaughterhouses reopening in Corpus Christi.

I pretty much was able to stay clear of politics, though I could be said to lean to the Democrats. Isolation was one of the benefits of being a couple of days ride from Corpus Christi and any other significant towns. I did hear that the Democrats were managing to beat back the post-war onslaught of carpetbaggers, scalawags, and Republicans by winning elections in their states. To my thinking, it didn't much matter here at the ranch. I heard rumblings about some terribly nasty anti-Reconstruction violence by a group called the Ku Klux Klan, but I never saw any of them or knew anyone who did. Had they been around, I believe I'd have resisted them. It wasn't exactly a glorious moment for the Democrats. With Michael gone and the war over, resorting to violence for political gain just didn't seem to be the answer.

It sure gave pause for a lot of reflection, as those years 1862 to 1865 truly shaped my future as defender, husband, parent, and rancher.

Nicholas Dunn (circa 1900)

(Dunn Family Photo)

Nicholas & Andree Ann Dunn (circa 1895)

(Photo: Dunn Family Archive)

Nicholas & Andree Ann Dunn's Burial Memorial
(Holy Cross Cemetery, Corpus Christi, TX)

(Photo by Mark Greathouse)

Ellen O'Toole Corrigan (Andree Ann Goebel Dunn's mother)
(Photo from "Texas-The Country and Its Men," 1915, L.E. Daniell)

Champion (World champion bred by Nicholas Dunn)
(Dunn Family Photo)

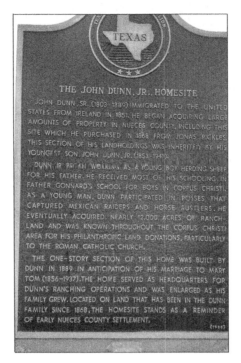

Texas Historical Marker for John Dunn, Jr
(Photo by Mark Greathouse)

John Dunn, Sr. (1803-1889) immigrated to the United states from Ireland in 1851. He began acquiring large amounts of property in Nueces County, including this site which he purchased in 1868 from Jonas Pickles. This section of his landholdings was inherited by his youngest son, John Dunn, Jr. (1853-1941).

Dunn, Jr., began working as a young boy herding sheep for his father. He received most of his schooling in Father Gonnard's School for Boys in Corpus Christi. As a young man, Dunn participated in posses that captured Mexican raiders and horse rustlers. He eventually acquired nearly 12,000 acres of ranchland and was known throughout the Corpus Christi area for his philanthropic land donations, particularly to the Roman Catholic Church.

The one-story section of this home was built by Dunn in 1889 in anticipation of his marriage to Mary Tom (1856-1937). The home served as headquarters for Dunn's ranching operations and was enlarged as his family grew. Located on land that has been in the Dunn family since 1868, the homesite stands as a reminder of early Nueces County settlement.

John Dunn, Sr. Home on Up River Rd, Corpus Christi, TX
Built on Property Acquired in 1852, Photo 1907
(Dunn Family Photo)

John Dunn, Sr., Father of Nicholas Dunn
(Dunn Family Photo)

THE ADVERTISER.
EXTRA.

W. H. MALTBY, - Editor.

CORPUS CHRISTI, TEXAS:

Wednesday, August 14, 1867.

OFFICE ADVERTISER,
CORPUS CHRISTI, Texas,
Aug. 14, 1867—12 M.

When, on the 27th ult., we last issued the ADVERTISER, how little we then dreamed of the dread calamity that hung over our City. When we made the call for an organization of the Howard Association, we did it from prudent motives, believing that every caution should be used to guard the public health. We were adverse to creating unnecessary public excitement, hence we made no mention of the existence of yellow fever. In fact, at that date, but few cases of fever had occurred, and they were not positively pronounced yellow fever.

But the cloud burst upon us—a disease of the most virulent and malignant character — and soon death after death occurred among our best and most valuable citizens, male and female, and up to the present time there has been no cessation. Our local physicians used all their skill and ability to check the disease, labored day and night, until they fell victims and died martyrs to the cause of humanity.

There is scarcely a house in the City that has escaped either sickness or death of some of its inmates. Our pen is inadequate to the task of describing the distress that now prevails among us.

The death of a wife and sister, the sickness of two other members of our family, and of ourself, must be the apology o our patrons for the suspension of our paper, and of this very brief notice of events

that have transpired since our issue of July 27th.

The following is a list of deaths that have occurred. It is possible that a few have been overlooked:

July 3—Mr. Snyder, came from Indianola, sick 1
.. 25—Mr. Drinkard, not fever, 1
.. 26—Rev. Wm. H. McPhail,
    Mrs. John Pollan, ... 2
.. 27—J. N. Morgan, ... 1
.. 28—Mr. Perry, a Pole, name
    unknown, Mr. Sterne.. 3
.. 30—H. H. Eastwood, ... 1
Aug. 1—Rev. Wm. Mitchell, ... 1
.. 4—Mr. Palmer ....
.. 5—Sam'l Clymer, Clayton,
    child of Mr. Larkin... 3
.. 6—Marcella Swift, Mrs.
    McClannahan, ... 2
.. 7—Mr. Smith, Pat'k Dunn,
    Daniel Cahill, a Pole,
    name unknown, Jane L.
    Marsh, Mrs. Christo-
    pher Dunn,.......... 6
.. 8—John W. Scott, Widow
    Clark, Christop'r Dunn,
    James Rankin, F. J.
    Cromer, Frank Still-
    man, H. Fisher, Rebec-
    ca Hughes (child), T.
    M. Lawrance,......... 9
.. 9—James Gibbs, Benjamin
    Gibbs, Mrs. Hughes, F.
    Riddir, Owen Clymer,
    Gregory Headen, Mc-
    Farlane, Miss A. Dann. 8
.. 10—Henry Sinclair, Carrie
    Sims, two Poles, (un-
    known), Mrs. John Kel-
    ly, — Kelly, (child),
    Chas. Fields, Dr. G. F.
    Johnston, Mrs. Mary
    Grace Maltby, George
    Mouly, Jas. Almond,
    Mrs. Charles Weiden-
    moeller, John Pollan,
    Jr., Dr. George Robert-
    son, Agnes Rankin,.... 15
.. 11—Mr. Stone, a Mexican,
    Lizzie Riger, Louisa
    Dryar, Mrs. Vetter, Mrs.
    Geo. A. Ludewig,......
.. 12—Dr. E. T. Merriman, A.
    DeRyee, Mrs Schultz, J.

M. Sims,............. 4
.. 13—Mrs. Matthew Headen,
    Mrs. Gibbs, Mrs. John
    Dunn, Mrs. F. Riddir,
    Joseph Dunn, J. M.
    Myers, George Adolphs
    Ludewig, infant of Dr.
    G. F. Johnston, Michael
    Whelan, Mrs. Michael
    Whelan,............. 10
.. 14—John Gallahan, Rinal-
    do Allen,............ 2
P. S.—7 more deaths as we
go to press, at 5 P. M.......... 7

Total to date,............. 83

THE LATEST.

CORPUS CHRISTI, Saturday, August 17, 2 P. M.—23 more deaths have occurred since the above date, 22 of fever. Number of interments to date, 106. We cannot furnish a full list of names. 6 new cases yesterday ; 1 reported to-day. We are informed that many old cases do not yield readily to treatment.

Letter to Correspondents of Howard Association.

To Dale & Ashworth, Thos. J. Poole, N. W. Woodman, F. E. Hughes, and others, individ.

Gentlemen—Your kind notes have been received. We are very grateful for your expressions of sympathy, and the material aid you send. The cloud of death still hangs over our devoted City. Many of our best citizens have fallen. Two resident Physicians, two resident Druggists, eight Merchants, five Undertakers, our acting Mayor, six Masons, are among the victims. Many families have been broken up. These facts will give you some idea of our present condition and suffering. All that the friends of humanity can do, will be required to relieve the needy and prevent further suffering. Any funds sent to Gen. E. J. Davis, Wm. Headen, R. Schubert, or myself, will be thankfully received and faithfully applied. J. P. PERRAN, President Howard Association.

[handwritten] Total deaths to date 109

[handwritten] 18th none
19th 3 deaths

The Advertiser, Corpus Christi, August 14, 1867
Lists five Dunn family yellow fever victims in 1867
(Corpus Christi Public Library Archive; Photo by Mark Greathouse)

Texas Historical Marker for Matthew Dunn
(Photo by Mark Greathouse)

A native of Ireland, Matthew Dunn was the first of five brothers to immigrate to the United States and settle in Corpus Christi. Their descendants have served prominently as active business and civic leaders throughout South Texas.

Upon his arrival in this country, Matthew Dunn enlisted as a sutler, or handler of goods, with Gen. Zachary Taylor. Taylor's army of occupation, at that time in New Orleans, was bound for Texas and arrived in Corpus Christi in 1845. Here Dunn met Col. Henry Lawrence Kinney who, having established a trading post, was encouraging settlement in the frontier town.

Kinney encouraged Dunn to send to Ireland for his four brothers. Between 1849 and 1868, Thomas, Peter, John, and Patrick Dunn migrated to Corpus Christi. In return, Kinney deeded some of his acreage, including the land around this site, to Matthew. He and his wife, Sarah (Pritchett) and three sons lived in the only house on the road between Corpus Christi and San Patricio.

Although neither a death date nor gravesite for Matthew Dunn has been found, he is important to local history as the leader of the immigration of his family to this part of Texas.

Author's Note: It is believed that Matthew Dunn died in Baton Rouge, LA in 1863.

John Beamond "Red John" Dunn, circa 1870
(Dunn Family Photo)

John Beamond "Red John" Dunn
Matt Dunn's Son and Nicholas Dunn's Cousin
(Corpus Christi Public Library Archive, "Perilous Trails of Texas;" by
John Beamond "Red John" Dunn; Photo copy by Mark Greathouse)

John F. Dunn (Nicholas Dunn's Rancher/Banker Son)
(South Texas Museum, Alice, TX; Photo by Mark Greathouse)

SEVEN

Cattlemen and Farmers

He keeps his saddle oiled and his gun greased.

Texas-ism

Following the wise teachings of my father, I had learned to keep several beeves as breeding stock to ensure a robust and growing herd of longhorns. The acreage of my ranch was plentiful, and we were blessed with some of the finest cattle and horses in southern Texas. Given the scrubby nature of what passed for pasture, it took a lot of acreage to raise a decent-sized herd of beeves. It tended to keep the already rangy-looking longhorns lean. The hardiness of these beeves compensated for their general lack of meatiness. I kept my eye on the goings on to the south as Richard King began experimenting with meatier but still hardy breeds.

Tilling the land turned out to be a quite productive exercise. The soil in parts of the Nueces River Valley, when properly tended, was so very rich. It seemed that just about anything could grow if you could get water to it. It made it easier to forget the famine years back in Ireland.

Andree Ann and I wasted no time continuing to build our family. She was ever the woman I first met with that demure smile and sweet Irish sense of humor. Andree Ann miscarried our second child, but in seeming rapid succession after Ellender "Nellie", we were blessed with Annie, Mary, John, Margaret "Maggie", and Teresa. Sadly, little Annie never made it to her first birthday. Her little life was taken on God's time, not ours.

We went about all those things that accompanied raising a family in a rough-and-tumble frontier environment. There seemed to be endless chores, but we never wanted for anything. Sometimes, it seemed hard to believe that we lived on the leading edge of civilization. That being said, there were regular reminders that we were, in fact, on the frontier.

My biggest challenge was going out most mornings to check cattle and horses on the various sections of the ranch. Of course, we were always on guard for the ever-dangerous Comanche, a few remaining Lipan Apache, Mexican banditos, and Anglo desperados on the run from justice. As I said before, we never ventured off very far alone. When we did, we were heavily armed. In the event of encounters with Comanche, it was generally advised to save a last bullet for yourself. Despite the tremendous opportunities in this land, the Nueces Strip was fully rife with all manner of danger and it pretty much bled over for many miles in just about any direction you might pick.

Determination, endurance, toughness. Those were qualities essential to survival on the Nueces Strip. There were countless human illustrations, but two stories about my brother John, Jr.'s bulldog served as anecdotal examples of those qualities. John raised sheep and had a large bulldog that he used to help with the herding. One day, a large buck came crashing out from a small clump of trees right next to that bulldog. The bulldog sprang at the deer and sank his teeth in one of the deer's flanks. The deer ran circles trying to shake the dog loose. At last, the deer fell from exhaustion. John, who had been yelling and following after deer and dog, approached the deer and slit its throat with his pocket knife. Despite the deer being dead, that bulldog wouldn't release its grip on the flank. John cajoled, persuaded, pulled, and finally had to use a stick to pry the dog's jaws from the deer. We'd laugh about it when we told family stories, but seriously admired the dogged determination of that bulldog. It was symbolic of what it took to make a life on the Nueces Strip.

A second incident cemented that bulldog's place in Dunn family lore. One summer night, that pooch was keeping a watchful eye on what he surely considered to be his sheep. Visualize a grassy meadow pasture bathed in moonlight and cooled by a light breeze. The sheep began to stir. They tended to be skittish anyway, but something had aroused them. The bulldog sensed it too and went off to investigate. He put his nose to the air and began to stealthily track a wide circle around that herd of sheep. It wasn't long before he encountered the source of the herd's concern. It turned out to be a large panther, or what some folks called a mountain lion. After barking a loud warning, that bulldog went on the attack and soon had the panther firmly by the throat. The blasted cat defended itself by clawing mercilessly at the dog's belly. John heard the commotion, grabbed a nearby pitchfork, and ran to rescue his dog. The bulldog and the panther were still locked in a vicious and deadly wrestling match with each other when he came upon the scene. He wasted no time and, at first opportunity, plunged that pitchfork into the panther with all the force he could muster. The beast finally breathed its last. But for its own wounds, the bulldog likely wouldn't have let go of that panther's throat. He was sliced up pretty badly by the cat's claws but, thankfully, John's bulldog recovered. The story needed no embellishment at family gatherings, and I think that bulldog was actually rather proud of those scars along his belly.

By way of dogged determination, it was part and parcel to the cattle business. There had been a significant lull in the cattle business toward the end of the War from 1864 through 1866 as prices plummeted. It was a matter of pent-up, post-war demand, coupled with a glut of beeves caused by the temporary suspension of the northward drives. Those danged longhorns were nothing if not prolific breeders. Herds grew rapidly. As I've said, they weren't the meatiest breed, but they were durable. Some ranchers tested the markets in Mexico and Louisiana, but those opportunities proved uneconomical. Major trail drives finally resumed in 1866, and we jumped on that trend. While there was still hostility from "Texas fever," the northern markets thrived and brought as much as $60 a head. The establishment of a marketplace and railhead at Abilene, Kansas finally eased the disease concerns.

Allow me to add here that around 1866, a fellow named Charles Goodnight invented a contraption we called the "chuck wagon." What an awesome convenience it was! Drawn by oxen or mules, it carried food, utensils, and a water barrel; tools to fix most anything encountered on the trail; stored the crew's bedrolls; and had a fold-out table for food preparation and service. Typical trail fare might include steaks, "chuck wagon chicken" (bacon), "sourdough bullets" (biscuits), and coffee so thick and rich you could just about stand a spoon straight up in the pot.

As I've said, I pretty much stayed at the ranch except for trips to buy and sell livestock. With a growing family, my droving days requiring extended periods away from home were pretty much done. Once a year, we'd bring in the yearlings for branding, and that was usually a family affair. As you might have gathered, the Dunn family was close, and we'd travel whatever distance was required to help each other with those yearlings and other ranching chores. You really needed to be there to fully appreciate a few dozen cowboys – or *vaqueros* – sorting out and lassoing beeves that had been driven in over the previous week or so. The longhorns had been out running wild and only occasionally coming together in small herds. Many got right ornery to say the least. Dust flew, hooves kicked, *vaqueros* shouted, and the wailing and snorting of the beasts could be almost deafening. To add to the utter chaos, there were always a couple of bulls that took more than a passing interest in the cows. These weren't just any bulls. They were huge and ready for breeding. As I described earlier, an adult longhorn bull with a six- to eight-foot horn spread might weigh more than 1,500 pounds. In any case, you didn't want to be in the way of one of those bulls as you wrangled and branded yearlings. I've seen men who weren't quick enough to get out of the way, and it was never a pretty sight. Understand, however, that despite an occasional cantankerous bull, longhorns could be pretty much domesticated. You could even saddle-ride the beasts, though the horns made that just a bit inconvenient. Nevertheless, you stayed clear if they got riled.

The best part of all of this round-up business was our families getting together for delicious meals, sharing our latest adventures, meeting the newest additions, and admiring the growth in size and responsibilities of the older children. Indeed, it was very much about family, and we never lost touch with our Irish heritage through music and stories. I must add that, with each passing year, there was less Irish brogue and more Texas twang in my own voice. This was especially so with the children. As to the Spanish language, try to imagine it with a touch of brogue and hint of twang. The Spanish-American Indian dialect was called *mestizo*. Those folks of that mixed heritage also made some of the finest *vaqueros*.

Ranching in South Texas – in fact, anywhere – demanded adaptation. A successful rancher had to be able to manage change, and I don't just mean weather. As an example, thanks in part to the previously mentioned cattle tick fever concerns, it wasn't long before we adapted and found ourselves driving our beeves the shorter distance to packing houses in Corpus Christi rather than the long riskier drives to the railheads in Kansas and Missouri. We also began to see economic pressure toward expanding the railroads in South Texas. All that beef from the packing houses needed to be transported, and railroads were a practical alternative to shipping out over the Gulf.

Slaughtering beeves was a nasty business – primarily for the beeves. A man with a heavy pointed shaft would drive the beeves under him down a chute, eventually stabbing them in the back of the neck to sever the spinal column. The dead beeves were gutted, skinned, and cut into shoulders, ribs, and various "delicacies." The hides would be stacked for tanning, and the tallow – essential for making candles and soaps – would be extracted from the meat via a boiling process. I won't go into further detail so as not to offend folks with more delicate sensibilities. However, it was all part of the business, right down to chowing down on delicious tender steaks slathered in tasty sauces of all sorts. There was nothing to compare to Texas brisket or chili.

Besides all that went into running the livestock portion of the ranch, we had to educate our young children. In our neck of the prairie, we didn't have a schoolhouse or schoolmaster to send them to. Fortunately, my mother kept a seemingly endless supply of books circulating through our home. I think it was partly Long Larry's influence, as he'd been intent on the Dunn family being well read. Every time Andree Ann and I visited my folks, we'd return with a load of books. This meant that Nellie, Mary, and John were reading at a very young age and would never be deprived of a book-learning education. I even recall a copy of the *Ben Hur* book that Lew Wallace fella had written.

My mother's influence – and her wisdom – were generously handed down. Thinking back, I recall one day back when I was around 20, I brought home a friend I'd had dealings with in Corpus Christi. The guy was overly nice, and that put my mom on her guard. She commented to me in an aside, "Nick, his halo fits too tight." I took it seriously then and looking back, truly appreciated her observation. He turned out to be a snake oil salesman of sorts.

Allow me to repeat here that Andree Ann was truly exceptional at caring for all the household operations. There was canning fruit, churning butter, milking cows, chasing chickens and gathering their eggs, making and repairing all manner of garments, tending gardens, washing, cooking, and more. We even found time for wine making. She killed coyote and fox a few times when I was away from the ranch. On one of my trips to Corpus Christi, I purchased a brand new 1873 Single Action Army Peacemaker for Andree Ann. It was Colt Firearm's latest masterpiece. Andree Ann made a point of practicing her marksmanship so she'd be able to defend our home if attacked while I was away on one of my business trips. Little wonder she was the love of my life.

For my part, I spent far too much time off buying and selling beeves and horses. When I was at home, I cared for the livestock, built and repaired fences and gates, and butchered a hog now and then. My father taught me the art of smoking hams, and I gained quite a reputation for that specialty. I guess it had to do with the wood, though I'll never reveal what I did special with it. Maybe you don't really want to know. Thank the Lord I had a couple of hired hands to help out with the big chores, or I'd have quickly worn myself to a frazzle.

Aside from round-ups and special events, pretty much the only times the family would get together was on Sundays. Now and again, we'd gather for weddings and funerals. It was a great time to share news about happenings in Corpus Christi and Brownsville. In fact, let me share my brother Mike's story such that you can better appreciate how we Dunns lived.

Mike was one of the finest men I ever knew, and I admired him nearly as much as my father. While he struggled with maintaining order in his life, Mike was nevertheless a natural-born gentleman. At about 3 inches over 6 feet in height, he was nearly as tall as my grandfather Long Larry. Mike weighed about 190 pounds and shared the family's tendency to fair complexion, red hair, and blue eyes. He walked with a slight limp because one of his legs had been broken three times in his youth. He had hard luck a couple of times with horses breaking down and falling on top of him. As a young man, Mike was of a sociable, friendly disposition, a good mixer, and enjoyed having a good time. He also drove some of Texas' finest buggy horses.

Horses were inseparable from his life. He always owned good saddle and buggy horses, no matter how low his fortunes were. It was a pleasure to see him on a horse, as he was a consummate horseman despite the aforementioned bad luck. Plus, his marksmanship with a pistol was equaled by few – except perhaps me. Remember, no blarney here.

In common with the other members of our family, he had that quick Irish temper, though he never held a grudge. Like our father and grandfather, he was a devout Catholic who practiced his faith in the finest way. He never accumulated wealth, as his complete honesty and charity came before the almighty dollar. Truth be told, it was unlikely that a man of Mike's character could ever amass riches. I thank God for giving me that kind of brother.

When Mike was 25 years old, he married Catherine Rose Whelan, age 18 years. She was a pretty girl with black curly hair, large brown eyes, and of medium height. She had the sweetest, most lovable disposition in the world and was welcomed into the family warmly by everyone, especially Andree Ann. The marriage was performed in our father's house.

Catherine had been left an orphan. Her parents were Denis and Anne Walsh Whelan, and they died when she was about two years old. Her grandparents journeyed from County Wexford, Ireland shortly after she lost her parents during the yellow fever epidemic of 1867, but they too died soon after. Her Uncle Michael Whelan, whom she idolized, cared for her and would have made her life happy as substitute parent, but he met his death on the battlefield during the Civil War.

My brother Mike's first home was on a 100-acre tract of land that he purchased for $500. It was adjoining our father's property. The house was well constructed, costing roughly $1,500 to build.

Like most of the Dunn family, Mike engaged in buying and selling livestock, especially horses, which he would ship all over the country, sometimes as far north as Iowa, Ohio, and Illinois. Arriving with his herd of horses at his destination, he would drive them through the countryside, putting on roping and riding exhibitions until his stock was all sold. I can verify that he was quite good at his craft. With his Irish resourcefulness and good-natured humor, he nearly always turned a profit.

Sometimes, even an expert can have bad luck. Once, he tried to bring home an expensive jackass for breeding purposes. He paid almost as much for the jack as he received for his bunch of horse stock that he had just sold. Please do understand that he had in mind to mate the jack with a mare and produce mules, hard-working but often stubborn offspring. Most mules were sterile, so keeping a prize jackass on hand to mate with mares was essential. On the trip, the jack got sick and wound up dying just three days after arriving home.

Mike never thought it was as funny a story as we made it out to be. It was just one of those things that characterized life in what really amounted to unpredictable frontier living. I suppose you had to be there to fully appreciate it.

While times were never easy, farming our local black soil was also very good. As I've said, soil was rich and quite fertile in many areas of South Texas. Mike's children got to enjoy life, as the nearby bay was full of fish, oysters, and shrimp. The family had a skiff, casting nets, fish lines, and plenty of guns. In the winter months, the bay was filled with wild ducks and the river flats two miles away were thick with wild geese. This was a hunter's paradise. There was no closed season, no limit to the kill. In the nearby brush, rabbits and birds were plentiful. If you could shoot, you'd never go hungry. However, as I've said before, we were ever reminded that we did live on the fringes of civilization.

Andree Ann and I lived in an utterly different environment from my brother Mike. The contrast was startling, as the vast and pretty much level prairie with its drier, rougher vegetation was our primary topographical feature, and water was found by digging wells and building cisterns.

As I described in an earlier chapter, my father raised Sea Island cotton. It was fine cotton for sure. While most every Dunn who owned property farmed a bit by necessity for food, we mostly raised longhorns and horses. It was a far cry from our livelihoods in Ireland, but a fresh start in a new land had demanded new thinking for a new destiny. Little wonder that I gained my reputation as a fair rancher and speculator in addition to Indian fighter and marksman. Of course, family was always our top priority just a notch below our Christian faith.

EIGHT

Texas Rangers & Banditos

"No man in the wrong can stand up against a fellow
that's in the right and keeps on a-comin'."
Captain Bill McDonald, Texas Ranger

Describing my life in Texas wouldn't be complete without sharing my thanks and admiration for the role of the Texas Rangers. It was also special to me because various members of my Dunn family either were Rangers or supported them. But for Andree Ann and all our children, combined with my love of raising beeves and horses, I might have become a Texas Ranger myself. Lord knows, I shared many of the same risks to life and limb as a rancher that those Rangers had to deal with in bringing law and order to the frontier. I implore you, readers of my story, to allow me to do honor in this chapter to the true legends of Texas: the Texas Rangers.

It must be remembered that the Mexicans were still smarting from their defeat in the Mexican-American War. While most Texas-resident Mexicans were a peaceful lot, there was still a significant amount of unrest among parts of the population. Thus, it was of little surprise that marauding bandits flourished under the leadership of rabble-rousing scoundrels like that Red Robber of the Rio Grande, Juan Cortina. There were certainly those who stayed in Texas and were overjoyed to be out from under the rule of Mexico's dictatorial presidents.

From what I'd heard, Mexicans tended to be conflicted between the freedoms of Texan social and political democracy with its economic success and their long heritage under the strict controls of monarchies, dominating presidencies, and dominatingly strong religion. It was as though they generally had a tough time simply accommodating liberty as Texans knew it. It often made for a polarized society in the Nueces Strip that would not quite be overcome in my lifetime. Guess it didn't help that many folks treated Mexicans as something less than human. Having experienced that sort of thinking from the British in Ireland, I found myself mostly sympathetic to our citizens of Mexican heritage. It simply didn't seem right to treat other humans as some sort of lesser beasts.

In my travels around the region, I learned this unrest had been going on since before Stephen F. Austin led early settlers into the Texas territory at the invitation of the Mexican government. It was apparently exacerbated by hostilities between the settlers and the likes of the Comanche, Kiowa, Karankawa, and Lipan Apache. The Mexican army was generally unavailable to provide the protection that Stephen Austin had been assured would be his. He knew that it would be impossible to attract settlers to Texas if the region was perceived as too dangerous. Austin decided to take matters into his own hands. Out of this situation had been born what would later become the Texas Rangers.

Little did I know that I would eventually have cause to be grateful to the Rangers, but that gets me just a tad ahead of myself.

By way of historical context, the first companies of what we would later refer to as the Texas Rangers were formed up way back in 1823 by a fellow named Moses Morrison, a lieutenant of Stephen Austin. They wouldn't actually be officially called Texas Rangers until about 30 years later, but at their time they were a force for peace. They earned about $15 per month payable in property, and their numbers varied as volunteers came and went. Keep in mind that Texas had no actual currency, so the only thing of value to pay these Rangers with was land. This having been said, and as I would learn, many of these hardy souls would make great contributions to the common defense of Texas settlements. Their cultural backgrounds included Anglos, Hispanics, and even non-hostile Indians. While most were born in the American South, many hailed from Ireland, Scotland, Germany, Holland, Italy, and England, so they spoke with a broad range of accents and dialects. While they had their individual stories of how they came to the United States, their common thread was that they were unified as Texas Rangers.

From the Indian hostiles, these Texas Rangers learned fighting tactics that would eventually serve them well in supporting the Texas War for Independence in 1836. In fact, their success with these fighting tactics would even influence those used by both Yankee and Confederate cavalries during the War Between the States.

Rangers were required to provide their own horses and equipment. At times, outnumbered in fights by as much as 50 to 1, it was common for each Texas Ranger to carry multiple pistols, rifles, and knives. These included Spanish-made pistols, Tennessee and Kentucky long rifles, and, later on, Sharps carbines. The favored revolver would eventually become the Colt, beginning with the Patterson and then the 1851 Navy. Some Rangers sported a rather menacing knife originally crafted in Sheffield, England and later made famous by Jim Bowie of Alamo fame. The name "Bowie Knife" caught on. The blade got ever fancier. The one Bowie made famous at the Alamo was impressive in size but not so pretty to behold.

Back in 1835, Texas settlers had enough of the Mexican government constantly violating their rights. They added insult to injury by suspending immigration from Europe and the United States. Texans were unhappy with the near-martial law imposed by President Santa Anna and his reneging on agreements made with Stephen Austin and codified in the Mexican Constitution of 1824. Right up to the first fighting for independence, Texans had hopes of a return to that 1824 agreement. With supposed assurance from the United States government that Texas would become annexed as a state upon its independence from Mexico, a movement began to gather steam. The Texas Rangers would have an important though not necessarily prominent role in supporting the war as they protected civilians retreating from Santa Anna's soldiers, harassed Mexican troops, and provided valuable intelligence. Notably, Rangers were quick to volunteer to join Colonel William Travis in the ill-fated defense of the Alamo in San Antonio.

After Texas independence on March 2, 1836, the Rangers continued their original mission of protecting settlers from marauding banditos and hostile Indians. But it took nine years for Texas to attain statehood. With Texas accepted in December 1845 as the 28th state to join the Union, the Rangers continued their vital protective role up to the events leading to the Mexican-American War.

You recall my earlier tale of my Uncle Matt having joined General Zachary Taylor's forces at Corpus Christi about this time. The Texas Rangers were an ever-present force that covered General Taylor's backside and kept General Winfield Scott's supply lines open. It is said that, at one point, Sam Walker and fifty of his Texas rangers held off an attack by more than 600 Mexican lancers, thanks in large part to being armed with Samuel Colt's improved Walker six-shot revolver. The Mexicans called the Texas Rangers "*Los diablos Tejanos*" or "Texas Devils." The performance of the cavalry-like Texas Rangers was enough that, by 1857, Secretary of War Jefferson Davis was inspired to create the first U.S. Cavalry units.

During the War Between the States, many Rangers joined the C.S.A. Cavalry (Mounted Rifles, as they were initially called), transitioning to military duties and necessarily ever less of their home security role. During Reconstruction following the War, they would be disbanded for a brief time since any Confederacy-linked civil or military authority was distrusted. Consequently, lawlessness flourished despite being under what was essentially martial law. Mobs – organizations dedicated to power through crimes like protection and blackmail – began to flourish on the Nueces Strip. The Ku Klux Klan made some trouble during Reconstruction, Comanche and Lipan Apache kept up sporadic attacks, the region was rife with desperados, and Mexican bandits seemed to be everywhere.

Following is a true tale of tragedy that was all too common for families in these days of post-war unrest and would eventually lead to greater activity from the Texas Rangers, not to mention anguish in the Dunn family.

On June 12, 1868, my brother Matt rode up to the house on the ranch he and my father owned. Of course, my father had his own spread, but he and Matt were always father-son close. It's the way our family was. Matt and he hired a bunch of Mexican *vaqueros* to do the day-to-day care of the livestock. The *vaqueros* were good at their craft, hard-working, and generally could be trusted. There was mostly mutual respect.

On this particular day, Matt found a bunch of Mexicans camped on the creek that ran not far from the house. He approached them warily, but they seemed to be a harmless friendly lot. He spoke fluent Spanish so was able to engage them quite fully. It should be noted that the ranch was well stocked at this time of year with cattle, horses, and sheep. Matt's horses were especially well cared for, as Matt also operated an overland mail route from Corpus Christi to Brownsville. A typical Dunn, Matt was quite the entrepreneur, always looking for ways to make money. A mail route made great sense.

Eventually, the Mexicans broke camp, mounted up, and rode the few hundred feet or so to the house to ask Matt for various things, such as salt, rice, and meat. Being a generous man, he gave them all the supplies they asked for. They even carried on a friendly conversation, laughing and joking in an almost happy-go-lucky manner. I have no idea what they talked about but can only guess it was the usual pleasantries folks encountered in these parts. There wasn't the slightest hint of any intended foul play. I gather that Matt wasn't the least bit suspicious. Apparently, the Mexicans told him that they were friends of his ranch foreman, Juan Franco. Matt counted on Juan's loyalty, so felt secure.

The next morning, my brother went off to attend Mass and then take part in a hunt for wild horses. He did not return until late in the afternoon. He uncharacteristically returned alone from the day's work. The Mexicans were still hanging around, by all accounts in a very bold mood likely enhanced by liquor. In fact, the booze probably made them far braver than they might ordinarily have been. Surely, they must have known of Matt's reputation as a marksman with a pistol.

I expect Matt gave the men his usual friendly smile. He dismounted, draping the reins nonchalantly over the hitching rail. He undoubtedly offered some friendly greetings about helping the Mexicans with anything they might need, so they could be on their way.

As he began to unsaddle his horse, one of them eased up behind Matt and shot him in the back of the head. I hear tell that he was killed instantly. My brother was only 27 years old. Some witnesses say that several of the Mexicans had cut him down in a hail of bullets, but in any case, Matt was dead. To my knowledge, it was a single shot that murdered him. It was learned afterward that Juan Franco, Matt's foreman, was the originator of the plot. So much for loyalty. The Mexicans robbed the place, taking everything of value including some of the best horses on the ranch, and then fled to Mexico. By good fortune, they never found Matt's stash of money – which would have been sizable, given that he had recently sold a considerable amount of cotton and several breeding horses.

Upon arriving at the ranch after a few days of being away, my father was horrified to come upon the havoc wreaked by those Mexican murderers. Matt's body was still lying in the dirt where he'd fallen. My younger brothers and sisters couldn't be protected from the tragedy. My mother especially would have been devastated had she still been with us, but she had succumbed to the yellow fever the year before. Matt had lost his wife Mary Ann and infant daughter Clara to yellow fever the year before. Tragedies of all sorts lay heavily on the family.

Of course, it was pretty much too late to do anything about the murder, and the Texas Rangers – which were not officially recognized as such at the time – were being kept on an extremely short leash by the powers that be in Austin. For all intents and purposes, the Rangers only existed in small informal bands or as individuals. It was post-War, money was tight, and politics were about as nasty as they could be. Politics played a big part as the Yankees recalled how effective the Confederate Cavalry, as manned mostly by former Texas Rangers, was at wreaking havoc on Federal troops. The intent was to keep the Texas population dependent upon Federal largesse. The situation was exacerbated by many of the policing forces installed by the Reconstruction government being former slaves. Many of these Negroes naturally were less than forgiving and had big chips on their shoulders.

I found myself frustrated and seething with anger over Matt's murder, and sought an opportunity to avenge his death. To their credit, one of these small troops of vigilante-style men that called themselves Rangers defied the government restrictions and stopped by Matt's ranch to investigate. Apparently, word of Matt's murder had spread around the Nueces Strip. I had been away on business when the attack on my brother happened, so I volunteered to join the Ranger posse upon my return. I figured my skill at tracking and my marksmanship might serve well.

There was no holding me back, and Andree Ann knew me well enough to not discourage my efforts. I was hot angry and ready to fight those Mexican bastards. A couple of our neighbors joined us, so we had a posse of eight heavily armed, outraged, revenge-motivated men.

We haltered some extra horses, and Andree Ann pulled together some grub for the trail. We were a fearsome-looking lot, to say the least. Pity those Mexican banditos if we ever found them.

I did learn that Cheno Cortina had been behind most of the raiding of ranches in between the Nueces River and the Rio Grande. He gave the bandits cover and, as I was told, used the Kickapoo Indians resident south of the Rio Grande to cover their tracks as they bolted into Mexico. Cortina had a habit of buying Indian loyalties, especially Apache. The Kickapoos were just another tribe benefitting from his largesse.

We tracked the Mexicans for about five days, but they had gotten far too great a jump on us. By the time we made it to the Rio Grande, they were already deep into the safety of their home country. If nothing else, the time spent with family and the Rangers on the manhunt helped ease the pain of Matt's death. I could take some small solace in having been involved in the task of having earnestly striven to catch his murderers. While there may have been some small comfort in the forgiveness that characterized my Christian faith, I prayed earnestly that those Mexican murderers would eventually be punished for their crimes.

I do have to admit, though, that it was tough not to paint the entire Mexican race with the deeds of those banditos. In truth, the Mexicans that turned to banditry were likely probably fueled by poverty and lack of opportunity, and they represented a small portion of the population, but that was hardly an excuse. There was also the ongoing frustration the Mexicans had at losing twice: first to *Los Diablos Tejanos* and then to the "*Norte Americanos*." Plus, there were the disruptions that came with often unstable governments in Mexico City. On the other hand, there was that element of the white population, especially around the Corpus Christi region and Nueces Valley – the Nueces Strip – that had no respect for the Mexican people and felt that killing them was no crime. Regardless of the Mexicans' motivations, their lawlessness – including thievery, murders, and kidnappings – was not forgivable.

Vigilante raids and lynching of Mexicans were not uncommon. Tough times indeed.

Overall, I felt blessed at having had the opportunity to work with the Texas Rangers during those brief few days hunting for Matt's murderers.

My brother Mike took charge of Matt's ranch and watched over our family interests. Mike wasn't an especially successful rancher, having experienced a couple of ranch failures, but he did a fair job of keeping an eye on the family legacy. Bandit raids continued intermittently, and everyone stayed on guard.

Around this time, a man named Hypolito Tapia sought work from my father. The family suspected that Hypolito might have been involved in Matt's murder, but proving it was another matter. They hired him just to keep him from running off. Despite this, roughly three months later, Hypolito Tapia didn't show up for work. We could only wonder at what he might have been up to.

Hypolito eventually returned and was rehired as a *rendador,* or expert trainer of horses, teaching them the finer points of neck reining that turned them into what they called cutting horses or chopping horses suitable for separating individual beeves from herds. The neck rein technique meant that the horse could turn instantly at a mere flick of the rider's wrist. Eventually, the horse would react as though instinctively. These horses with my father's JD brand became highly sought after.

Hypolito's sporadic and unaccountable absences continued. A long article in the local newspaper told of a murder at Peñascal at Laguna Madre around sixty miles away. The murder of four men was attributed to Comanche, but the evidence wouldn't support a Comanche-style attack. The Comanche were known to inflict horrific tortures and take scalps. These men had been shot multiple times after they had been bound so as to be incapable of self-defense. Whoever did the murders celebrated at the victims' home by getting beastly drunk and eventually hauling off all the goods they were able to carry. There were a couple of more instances of these terrible murders, including a Mr. Murdock who was chained to his bed while his house was burned down around him.

When word got back to me, I took note that these grisly murders coincided with Hypolito's absences. My brothers John and Mike joined with our cousins "Red John" Dunn and his brother Matt, riding to San Patricio County to find Hypolito's brother Manuel. Four friends eventually joined us on the investigation. Along the way, we encountered a man who seemed a tad suspicious. We suspected he might be familiar with the comings and goings of folks around the area so asked him where Manuel Tapia could be found. The man revealed himself by trying to escape, but we held him at gunpoint and threatened to hang him if he didn't tell us where the Tapias were. To loosen his tongue, we even threw a rope with a hangman's noose over a tree limb. He told us that Hypolito, Manuel, and three men had fortified themselves in a solid log pen used for sheep shearing. The pen was built around a hackberry motte. We were fully ready for action, as our posse was well-armed with Winchesters and pistols.

We took the captive Mexican with us, threatening him with instant death if he gave away our approach. Our posse split into two groups, entering on either side with pistols cocked. My brother John, Jr. found himself face to face with Hypolito Tapia, who was standing guard while the others slept. Hypolito moved toward a rifle leaning against the hackberry tree, but John aimed his pistol at him and Hypolito stopped cold in his tracks. He was not so stupid as to test John, Jr.'s trigger finger. The bandits were promptly awakened by our posse without incident. We tied them up, put them all on horses, and took them to a settlement called Meansville.

Upon news getting out about the arrests, a lynch mob quickly formed. Five new ropes with hangman's nooses were at the ready. Hypolito was so fearful that he almost instantly confessed to the

Peñascal murders so long as we didn't give him over to the mob. Eventually, each of the gang confessed. The crowd still sought to lynch them, so John, Jr. and Mike stepped in and told them that the murderers would be taken to Corpus Christi and hung legally. They threatened to shoot members of the mob if it became necessary. I should add that we had even gone to the trouble of obtaining a warrant to make the arrests legal.

The prisoners were transported to Corpus Christi that night with the aid of the Texas Rangers. During the journey, Hypolito convinced the sheriff that only he and a man named Andres Davila had committed the murders, so Manuel and the other two were turned loose. This action by the sheriff enraged the citizens, especially when it was learned that Manuel Tapia was wearing the coat of one of the murder victims. After all our efforts, we were not exactly pleased with the sheriff and I let him know it. It was a local jurisdiction matter, so even the Rangers' hands were tied.

Hypolito and Davila were tried in a court of sorts. Part of the evidence, in addition to the confessions, were serial numbers from the rifles stolen from the victims. During the trial, Hypolito's mistress tried to slip him a fig that contained arsenic, but she was caught. Both men were sentenced to hang. The day before the execution, a local priest, Father Jaillet, married Hypolito and his mistress. She turned out to be the mother of his three children. Guess it was the civilized thing to do by way of making the children legitimate.

Several hundred citizens witnessed the hanging. They'd erected a scaffold at the northeast corner of the courthouse. A guard of 40 men was present in the event of any crowd problems. A little before two o'clock in the afternoon, the men climbed the scaffold. Hypolito gave a short speech claiming his innocence, but stepped back quietly and even adjusted the noose placed around his neck apparently to make it more comfortable. The 7-foot drop broke the men's necks, killing them instantly. After about 15 minutes, the bodies were released from the nooses, placed in coffins, and given over to their families. Such was justice on the Nueces Strip. It was generally prompt. You'd have thought the likelihood of getting hung would pretty much dissuade lawbreakers, but it seemed they were never the brightest sorts.

Texas Rangers and banditos were indeed as much part of the Texas landscape as prairie grass and longhorns.

In an effort to put all the stresses of family tragedy behind me, I turned to joining a cattle drive to the railheads in Kansas. While the Comanche were in decline, they nevertheless made drives potentially quite hazardous. With my reputation as a Comanche fighter, I was suddenly in demand. By now, Andree Ann and I had a growing family to care for, so I initially only joined the one drive. Being away for two months or more on the trail wasn't especially desirable for folks raising families. However, we needed income. I joined additional drives but found myself seeking alternatives for getting beeves to market and involved myself in more livestock speculation.

NINE

The Yellow Fever

He eats sorrow by the spoonful.

Life in South Texas wasn't all peaches and cream, though we tried our best to make it so. Post-war Corpus Christi recovered surprisingly quickly, and its environs soon throbbed with commerce. The packing houses and stockyards flourished, as the city became a key hub for hides, tallow, and cattle by-products. The first formal schools that had opened a decade or so earlier thrived, the port had developed despite shallow channels, and the population was steadily growing. In fact, nearly a third of the residents was foreign-born. Oh, and men outnumbered women, making for an interesting social dynamic as men competed for eligible ladies to marry and raise families. With the vastness of the lands to the west, it was still fairly easy to become an owner of sizable property if you were of such a mind. It's important to note that land was like an official currency in Texas in the sense that it was often used as payment for services. For example, back after the Texas fight for independence, our fine soldiers were paid in land grants and early on the Texas government paid Texas Rangers with land.

The regional economic recovery after the War Between the States was driven largely by robust trade in the cattle industry, as well as trade in sheep and horses. Cotton production had slowed during the War but made a strong comeback, as well. The hostile Indians had ever less impact on the region, but there was another factor that was enough of a scourge to significantly impact economic development: yellow fever. As I describe here, the number of victims in Corpus Christi as a percent of the population of the city in 1867 – about 13 percent as I heard it – was devastating in and of itself.

Depending on the individual, the disease began with fever, perhaps a headache, reddened eyes, and then chills, back pain, and severe fatigue. It progressed to loss of appetite, nausea, and vomiting. For a few, however, it entered a toxic phase with jaundice, liver damage, and blood-laced vomit. The Mexicans called it *vomito negro,* or black vomit.

The year featured an unusually dry summer. When it did rain, the dry ground didn't absorb the runoff, allowing for fetid pools of rainwater and near-empty cisterns. Citizens had no idea that these provided fertile breeding ground for what I understood years later to be the *Aedes aegypti* mosquito. Only the females bore the yellow fever virus, but that was more than enough. Keep in mind that folks were still ignorant of this cause. It would be another 40 years before yellow fever was linked to mosquitos, so most Texans blamed the yellow fever on what they called a "miasma," a pollution in the air. I recall that miasma being cited as cause for the potato blight back in Ireland. Seems people often grasp at mystical causes of bad things, and something like this miasma fit their view.

The disease apparently originated in Africa and – thought by some folks as a punishment from God – was spread to America through the slave trade in the 17th century. Roughly half of those infected in the 18th and 19th centuries died. It was devastating from both humanitarian and economic perspectives. Increased trade in coffins and funerals was a tragic outcome. Few families were untouched by the disease. Recall my sharing how several of our family, including me, dealt with yellow fever back in 1863 and the death from it of my Uncle Thomas and my father's hired hand.

Businesses throughout Corpus Christi were shuttered and commercial, civic, and social activity necessarily came to a halt. People who tried to go to other towns often encountered armed guards with orders to stop anyone from Corpus Christi by deadly force if necessary. Sadly, fear had a way of exacting such behaviors.

In August 1867, my mom, brother Christopher and his wife, and my brothers Patrick and Joseph died of yellow fever during this epidemic. Nearly our entire family was stricken with the disease at the same time. As I've mentioned, my now deceased brother Matt lost his wife Mary and their infant daughter.

At the time of their deaths, Christopher was 34, Patrick 32, and Joseph 24. Joseph had the ill luck of having been home from seminary when he was stricken. Many families in the region were ripped apart by the disease, as the damnable affliction wasn't particular about who it took.

I do find it obligatory to share my dear mother's tragic bout with yellow fever as it was told to me. To put it in perspective, many folks back in Ireland belonged to the non-monastic group of the Franciscans known as the "Third Order." Except for certain very special religious occasions, the brown-hooded habit that characterized the group was not worn. It was stored away such that, at death, the member's body could be wrapped in it. It sounds a bit macabre, but there were a lot of folks who strongly ascribed to its power and symbolism. So, when my mother had contracted the yellow fever and was confined to her bed, my fourteen-year-old brother, John, Jr. – who earnestly believed she would recover – spent much time with her. After all, she was a hardy Irishwoman, having birthed nine children, survived a three-month voyage from Ireland, helped my father build a home on the Texas frontier, and offered naught but warmth and security to family and friends. How could such a loving, giving person possibly die of some horrific pestilence?

Nevertheless, one day she summoned young John to her bedside, laid a frail and exceedingly warm hand on John's, and asked that he bring her the Third Order robe. He fought back tears as he mounted his saddle horse, rode at breakneck speed, and fetched the robe from the Whelan's house about three miles away. When he returned with the robe, our mother had already died. Her passing was a huge loss for our family. I was heartbroken to have not been near when she contracted the disease. As God-loving and strong as she was, I had been confident that she would endure. Moreover, my mother was the family "glue," as she coordinated myriad social gatherings, kept track of birthdays and anniversaries, and always offered a warm and welcoming home to all.

I expect that Andree Ann and I were lucky to be living farther away from Corpus Christi on drier lands, so we unwittingly missed the wrath of the yellow fever scourge of 1867. We kept fires going near the house, thinking the smoke might prevent the dread miasma. Still, it was sad to see family burial plots expanding far too quickly. Each loss of a loved one hurt, yet it was hard not to develop a pain-numbing stoicism about so many losses.

With the onset of cooler weather, the chill put a stop to further spread of the yellow fever. Estimates placed the death toll at roughly 127 of the city's 1,000 residents. Unsurprisingly, few folks felt led to joyfully celebrate Thanksgiving in Corpus Christi in 1867.

The yellow fever was also becoming a scourge of the region's indigenous tribes of Karankawas, Lipan Apache, and Kiowa, as well as some of the Comanche. The tribes simply had built no immunity to what they called the "white man's disease." In addition to yellow fever, cholera caused by compromised water sources had a disastrous effect in wreaking its deadly outcomes mercilessly.

The diseases, in combination with the beginnings of the buffalo slaughters, were taking a heavy toll on the indigenous tribes. The Comanche culture was especially linked with the buffalo. Coupled with an overwhelming ever-westward onslaught of settlers, their days of enjoying the unbounded freedom of the Comancheria were fast disappearing. It also made them more desperate.

This meant that we were ever more vigilant. While the yellow fever may have missed my own little family, thanks to us being on our ranch far from the outbreak, the threats of Mexican banditos and lingering tribal war parties still could not be ignored. I always kept a pistol in my holster and tried to keep a rifle nearby. We also mounted a couple of loaded rifles near the doorway to our house and at the barn, high enough, of course, to be out of reach of our youngest children. It was an inevitability that lots of folks in the region would face, and we were no exception. I recall my father and my Uncle Matt telling me of having to hide from Comanche on several occasions.

It was about this time in 1868 that my Uncle Patrick became the fifth and last of Long Larry Dunn's sons to immigrate to Texas. Born in the Townland of Killeigh in County Kildare in 1801, he brought his second wife Mary Anne and his nine children with him. He built a home on a 163-acre farm west of the McBride's in Nueces County. Already in his 60s, Patrick was no spring chicken, but he worked hard and carved a life out of the Texas frontier. Importantly, Patrick brought the news of the passing away of my grandmother Ellen in Dublin in 1864. It was sad to hear the news, and with it came the realization that we truly would never be going back to Ireland. That curtain had been brought down. My grandparents had lived long lives under challenging circumstances, but had endured despite the British occupiers and potato famines. They'd borne witness to most of their sons settling far from home in Texas. I am convinced that it was their unselfish love and great vision for the future that gave them the strength to urge their sons to immigrate to America. They understood far better than most folks that a destiny was at stake.

To be clear, by this time, if asked my identity, I would unhesitatingly call myself a Texan. My brogue was an ever-more fleeting affectation, as I found myself drawing out my vowels and truncating my words more along the lines of the sing-song twang that Texans would become noted for. I expect I found myself preferring its melodic tones.

Texas was beginning to recover from the War. By example, wool production at my father's place was reaching an all-time high. It was about economic diversification. In October 1873 alone, our family records show that we sheared 1,184 sheep, producing seven sacks of wool weighing more than 2,000 pounds in total and bringing in $521.50. To further illustrate how sheep raising was contributing to the local economy, the Corpus Christi Gazette on April 24, 1873 wrote:

> *This week we had the pleasure of examining samples of wool clipped from the imported Cotwold bucks of Capt. R. King. Measuring seven inches in length; and from a five-months-old lamb, a cross between a Cotswold and a Merino, measuring five inches in length... notwithstanding the low prices being paid at present, numerous loaded trains of carts are constantly arriving in Corpus Christi with wool. Already one firm in our city has shipped upwards of 400,000 pounds...The stock raisers of this section are being gradually awakened to the importance of raising fine sheep.*

> *It now forms the largest part of the stock interest of this section... The leading breeders...have made during the past year important purchases of blooded bucks, imported from the states of Pennsylvania, Ohio, and New York. The sheep industry in Nueces and adjoining counties may now be said to be in a flourishing condition.*

I must add that ever more land in the region was being partitioned and fenced off, making the raising of beeves a tad more challenging.

It would be another decade before the arrival of barbed wire, but the trend of defining boundaries and controlling access to precious water had begun.

TEN

Comanche Raid

"Me and Red Wing aren't afraid to go to hell together. Captain Jack, he's too mucho bravo. He's not afraid to go to hell all by himself."

Apache warrior Flacco, Jack Hays' second-in-command

Bert – that was short for Bertram – stirred in the corral as the rays of the sun bore down, warming his ample coat and taking away the morning chill. He turned as if to fully absorb the warmth and flicked a couple of flies with his tail. Bert. He was my prize longhorn breeder bull. He likely weighed a tad more than 1,600 pounds and sported a horn span of better than 8 feet tip to tip. He could be right friendly, but you didn't get between him and a cow when it was mating season. I was hanging by the corral gate alongside the water trough and preparing to feed the big guy. He was being his normally docile self, a condition that belied the raw power he possessed.

Bert suddenly stuck his nose straight up, flared his nostrils, and then dropped his head and bellowed. I heard horses galloping behind me and reflexively dropped behind the water trough. I slipped off my hat and cautiously peeked my head above the edge of the trough.

Thwump! The arrow stuck in the fencepost inches from my head. A second whizzed under my elbow, and a third swooshed past my ear. The air was pierced with all manner of whooping and yelling. Dust flew everywhere.

"Andree Ann...Nellie! Stay in the house!" By the time I'd unholstered my revolver, another arrow went through my shirtsleeve and nicked my arm as I dove even lower behind the water trough. More arrows hit the trough or whizzed by my ears. With the noises of war whoops and horse hooves, it seemed as though an entire tribe had descended upon us. Obviously, these savages weren't aware of my cattle drive exploits.

I knew Andree Ann would have the sense to grab a rifle and stay under cover in the house, but I worried whether my daughter, Nellie, might peek out and be in harm's way. I didn't need her showing off for her brother and sisters. By now, I'd counted at least six Comanche warriors and had managed to seriously wound at least one. From my experience fighting them, I right quickly figured out that they were Comanche by the way they rode as one with their ponies, the broad black war paint stripes that swept menacingly across their faces, and the elaborate nature of the regalia they wore. They'd been shooting arrows at me, but none had as yet come close enough to count coup, the practice of showing bravery by touching their enemy and running off before returning for the kill.

From the stories we had heard, there was no way I could permit my family to be taken captive. As I've described earlier, Comanche torture was legendary in its horror. There was no way I'd let them take my wife and little ones. This was a fight to the death. By my way of thinking, it would be theirs.

The Comanche were fearless fighters and exceptional horsemen. In fact, many military folks thought they were the best mounted fighters in the world. A tribe typically held several hundred head of ponies. Horses were a measure of Comanche wealth, and a powerful chief might have a hundred or more. As to Comanche fighting tactics, even the U.S. Army had failed time after time to cope with their prowess. That disadvantage wouldn't last long, as Union Army Colonel Ranald Slidell MacKenzie proved soon enough. Notably, the Texas Rangers had proven years before under Captain Jack Hays that the Comanche were no match for brave, aggressive men led by fearless leaders and armed with those famous Colt revolvers and breech-loading Sharps rifles. In part, Hays had honed his fighting tactics as one of the heroes of San Jacinto back in the Texas War for Independence. MacKenzie, on the other hand, had earned his reputation on the battlefield during the War Between the States. As to me, you recall I applied those same Jack Hays tactics fending off attacks during cattle drives to the Kansas and Missouri railheads.

By way of reminder, recall the strategy I shared back on the cattle drives, when the Comanche would try to lure drovers into an ambush before doubling back and stealing horses. They had refined that technique against mounted military troops.

The Comanche battle tactics against mounted troops were actually simple. Typically, the Comanche, occasionally along with their Kiowa allies, would draw troops into a protracted chase staying just out of their reach. Eventually, the sun would set. Once the troops had been forced to dismount and bivouac, the Comanche would attack at night, steal the horses, and leave the cavalry on foot in remote wilderness areas often subject to harsh weather extremes. Notably, it was said that Texas had four seasons: drought, flood, blizzard, and twister. None were great options. The Comanche generally stayed west of that imaginary line – that 98th meridian I mentioned – that ran through Fort Worth and Austin, but that's an immense area. To make dealing with the Comanche even more challenging, they were comprised of as many as 13 separate tribes. Peace with one tribe was no guarantee of peace with the others. Also, the Comanche were one of the few tribes that moved at night. We felt especially vulnerable when the moon was full. In fact, we commonly referred to the full moon as "the Comanche moon."

While this gives you a sense of the reputation and prowess of the Comanche, and I appreciate your indulgence, there was an immediate crisis at hand. I knew the Comanche were primarily after my horses, if not our scalps. As I rightly feared, they would likely not mind killing us or taking our children captive – especially the young girls. They wasted no time opening the gate to the horse corral.

Praying that my family was staying inside the house, I felt free to unleash what firepower I had. Arrows seemed to be flying everywhere. How could half a dozen Comanche unleash such a barrage? I was amazed that the warriors could fire arrows with reasonable accuracy and quickness while ducked down along the side of their horses, placing the horse between them and their target. However, I had no time to pause in admiration, and there was certainly no time to grab one of the other rifles we had stowed for just such an emergency.

The Comanche warrior who appeared to be their leader was impressive in his full black war paint, feathered headdress, lance, and shield. While small of stature, he was a fearsome sight astride his pony. In retrospect, I'd describe him as of a wiry build. He had a cold wildness in his eyes that would likely as not get even the bravest man's hair standing on end and send a chill up the spine. I'll never forget my eyes meeting his steely gaze.

Fortune and what turned out to be my own excellent marksmanship served me well this day. I blew another Comanche off his horse with a torso shot at close range. He was dead before he hit the ground. I wounded at least two others, and they finally took off with about four of my best horses. The chief stopped and turned his pony for a moment, stared intensely back at me, nodded almost admiringly, let out a final guttural shout, and galloped off.

At least, Andree Ann and the children were safe – or so I hoped. With the Comanche on the run, I bolted for the barn, grabbing a rifle hung inside the door, then headed for the house moving quickly from cover to cover. As I leaped onto the gallery and reached the door of our house, I paused. Three arrows were embedded in the door and door jam. The silence was deafening. I pushed the door gently, and it creaked open. Andree Ann was standing before me with the Winchester rifle braced against her hip and a never-to-be-forgotten wild look in her eyes. The children were hiding behind the overturned table, while young Nellie stood with an axe at the ready. "It's over," I exhaled as a wave of nausea overtook me.

Andree Ann dropped the rifle and collapsed into my arms. "Who? What?" Then, as she saw my torn and bloodied shirtsleeve, "Are you all right?" Frontier life tended to make us all a bit hardened to emotion, but Andree Ann could not hold back tears of relief. The frontier tended to toughen folks, but now and again there was pause for tears, be they joy or sadness or – in this case – relief. I recall holding her for a long time as she buried her face in my chest.

Just as I thought we could relax, I heard riders approaching. Looking over my shoulder through the open door, I quickly made out that they were not Comanche. Desperadoes? Banditos? Definitely sounded as though the mounts were shod.

Andree Ann retrieved the rifle, and I quickly reloaded my pistol and held my rifle at the ready. I nudged Andree Ann behind me and moved to the door. The children stayed hunkered down behind the table. Even Nellie saw fit to drop the axe and join them. I inched cautiously out onto the gallery with Andree Ann close behind me.

Four riders pulled up at our gate. "Y'all the Dunns?"

I nodded and hollered. "What's your business?" Just then, I recognized Leander McNelly from pictures in the Corpus Christi newspaper. He'd been a hero during the War Between the States and was now an ever-more-famous Texas Ranger. While they had been disbanded for a time, the Texas Rangers were now being reauthorized.

"Rangers," shouted the lead horseman. "My name is McNelly. Y'all okay?"

I motioned them to approach. They dismounted and led their horses in. McNelly especially was expertly eying the area around the house. I'd already heard of Captain McNelly and his Special Force aimed at cleaning up what was left of Cortina's mobs and other thieves and desperadoes ranging between the Nueces River and Rio Grande. The vastness of the Nueces Strip tended to give cover for the evil folks among us.

"Small party from the number of arrows. I see you got one of them." He measured his words, as he nodded toward the Comanche warrior lying face down in the dust near the water trough. His words were drawn out in the Texas drawl we had become used to. "That likely saved your lives. Is anyone hurt?"

"No, we're fine, Captain." My ever-present Irish brogue mixed with Texas twang contrasted to McNelly's much slower voice cadence. I noted that he wasn't physically impressive, but I'd heard that his Texas Rangers deeply admired his leadership style. By this time, the children had shuffled out onto the gallery that extended across the front of our house. I breathed deeply, as I began to more fully grasp what had happened. "They got away with some of our horses."

"Likely as not, they were part of Také-vera's band. The arrows are all Comanche, so it looks as though no Kiowa were with them. Most of the tribes have gone to what are called reservations in Oklahoma Territory, and Buffalo Hump is no longer a concern. Can't figure what this bunch is doing so far from the Llano. Must be desperate."

Andree Ann scanned the yard and stepped back in horror when she spied the dead Comanche.

McNelly was quick to respond, "Don't worry, Mrs. Dunn, ma'am. We'll take care of him." McNelly knew there was a bounty on any dead Comanche.

I was pleased to let the Rangers dispose of the dead savage. I felt blessed at not having to deal with that nasty task. "Do you think they'll be back?"

"I expect they've had enough of you, Mr. Dunn," offered McNelly admiringly. "Like I said, they've stretched far outside their usual territory." As I described before, their "usual" territory, or Comancheria, stretched from the Platte River to the Rio Grande and from the aforementioned 98th meridian west beyond the Llano Estacado near the Palo Duro Canyon. McNelly continued, "Mr. Dunn, didn't you join up with a posse of Rangers to chase some Mexicans a while back? You're Matt Dunn's brother, right?"

"Yes, sir, that's a fact."

"Well, I know you caught up with a couple of them, but not all. Some of my Rangers did catch up with a couple of those murdering banditos a couple of weeks ago about two days ride south of here. That's at least two that won't be bothering law-abiding citizens anymore." McNelly didn't say what became of the captured banditos but, given the vigilante-style justice increasingly meted out in the region, they would have been lucky to have only been lynched. "Sorry about your brother, Mr. Dunn."

"We appreciate that, Captain." I winced as I extended my wounded arm to shake his hand.

McNelly sized me up. "You're a pretty fair marksman, Mr. Dunn. I'd heard of your exploits fighting off Comanche on trail drives. It's tough to get off accurate shots under pressure. I expect you're now strong medicine in the eyes of the Comanche." McNelly knew of what he spoke, having taken the measure of a few Union soldiers as well as Apache and a passel of Mexican bandits. It was a huge compliment coming from the captain.

Captain McNelly motioned his men to load the Comanche warrior's body onto their pack horse. One of the feathers from the warrior's lance pirouetted to the ground, and Nellie – to the bemusement of the Rangers – darted out to grab the trophy. "We'll be moseying now, folks. I'm sure they won't be back." McNelly mounted, turned slightly in his saddle, and looked down at me. "We're heading back toward Corpus. We'll let the folks there know what happened here and that y'all are safe."

I knew that Captain Leander McNelly was the toughest of the tough, having gained an impressive reputation for showing no mercy to hostile Indians, marauding rogue Comancheros, Mexican banditos, and any miscreants that ran afoul of the law…such as it was. Comancheros, by the way, were Mexican traders who earned their name by trading with the Comanche. They were also a savage lot by any measure.

What I didn't know was that McNelly's Texas Rangers had buried a family at a nearby homestead the day before. Those folks had ranched and farmed a spread a day's ride southwest of us and had been hit by a larger band under Také-vera, the main chief of what remained of the Penateka Comanche after Buffalo Hump died. Buffalo Hump, incidentally, got his name because of his deformity, a large hump on his back. Také-vera had made a loose alliance with Costalites, chief of the Lipan Apache that ranged from northern Mexico through South Texas. Owing to shrunken territories and reduced populations, the tribal lines did blur a bit, as the Lipan Apache were also now allied with the Mescalero and Chiricahua Apache of Cochise and Geronimo fame. The Comanche had reverted to using traditional arrows and lances, since bullets had become difficult to acquire.

Captain McNelly's reputation was growing by the day along what was called the Nueces Strip. By way of further explanation and at the risk of repeating myself, the Nueces Strip – also called by some the Wild Horse Desert – is the area of South Texas stretching from the Gulf of Mexico to the headwaters of the Nueces River and between the Nueces River and the Rio Grande. The Republic of Texas had claimed the Rio Grande as its southern border, while Mexico claimed the Nueces River roughly 150 miles to the north. The Nueces Strip had been formally ceded to the United States by the Treaty of Guadalupe Hidalgo in 1848 after the Mexican-American War.

The Nueces Strip became the focus of what in later years might have been called organized crime. A strikingly handsome 25-year-old John King Fisher was leader of a large band of rustlers and cutthroats that roamed far and wide over the Strip terrorizing the population. I understand from news accounts that Fisher had a modest ranch on Pendencia Creek in Dimmit County that served as his headquarters. At any given time, 40 to 50 of his gang would be close at hand. Fisher always wore only the very finest clothing and had the most beautiful women at his disposal. His horses and tack were invariably the very best. He likely had his pick of horses stolen in Mexico – called "wet stock," as they had been swum across the Rio Grande.

One of Captain McNelly's prime tasks was to bring John King Fisher to justice. On May 28, 1876, McNelly led a force of 40 Texas Rangers against Fisher's ranch. Just a few weeks earlier, Fisher and a murderer and rustler named Burd Obenchain had stolen a herd of cattle from six *vaqueros* near Eagle Pass, killed all of the Mexican cowboys, and buried them in a single grave. Now, McNelly was set to attack Fisher's spread. At a signal, McNelly's Rangers charged at both sides of Fisher's main ranch house, catching his gang totally off guard. The Rangers quickly secured the ranch and arrested Fisher and his gang. Apparently, the gang was actually relieved to learn that they were captured by Rangers and not members of one of the vigilante groups known to roam the region. They might have been lynched immediately had that been the case.

I should add that Captain McNelly had a very effective policy for ensuring that his captives always reached their destination. He would tell his Rangers within earshot of the captives that if any prisoner attempted to escape or there was any attempt at rescue, the Rangers were to kill them without warning or mercy. This was known on the frontier as *la ley de fuge*, the shooting of escaping or resisting prisoners. It apparently was very effective.

McNelly would go on to spend nearly another year with mostly success at wiping out crime on the Nueces Strip. His contribution was extremely valuable toward the development of the region. He passed away from tuberculosis on September 4, 1877 in Burton, Texas, up in Washington County. He was only 33 years old. Texas lost a great Ranger and patriot.

The day following the Comanche raid at my ranch, my brothers John and Michael came by to visit along with my father. They acted casually, but we knew it was to check on us and how we had fared. Andree Ann and the children were still a bit shaken, though by this time Nellie had collected a handful of trophy Comanche arrows to show off to her grandfather and uncles.

Andree Ann marked the occasion by cooking a feast worthy of celebrating our survival. We recounted the attack *ad nauseum*, as our story was ever more embellished with each telling. The family picnic was in Corpus in a couple of months, and the story was sure to improve with age.

I penned a letter to my cousins still back in Kildare. As a bit of good Irish fun, I sent a clipping from a horse mane and told them it was from a Comanche scalp. I'm sure they never figured out my joke. Had my grandfather Long Larry still been around, he'd have been overjoyed at my tales. I assured them that we were ever the measure of the Comanche warriors. They were already aware that, while the British wreaked terrible tortures and hardships on the Irish, they were not quite so bad as the Comanche. Pardon my repeating it, but keep in mind that the Comanche would perform unspeakable horrors on captives, scalping adults while still alive, cutting off private body parts, raping women, and more.

ELEVEN

Ambush

This ain't my first rodeo.

Texas-ism

By now, my family had blossomed to six little Dunns, though we had lost little Annie and two more infants that Andree Ann miscarried. So, I guess that makes nine officially. I must say that we felt as though God had indeed watched over us, and we enjoyed His bounty. With the Comanche raid well behind us, we settled into relative normalcy. We knew better than to let our guard down – mostly.

Yearling time was approaching, and I took time from my cattle-speculating and horse-trading trips to help patrol the farthest reaches of the ranch to find strays. I'd sold my ranch near Beeville and bought up nearly 15,000 acres about a dozen or so miles west of Corpus Christi. As you might imagine, 15,000 acres of sprawling prairie covered in all manner of wild critters and rough vegetation presented a prodigious task for finding and tending livestock. Recall that it took quite a bit of acreage of grass and scrub to adequately feed a single scrawny longhorn. Also, I'd begun a commitment to ship 100 head of beeves each week to New Orleans via the steamer Aransas. This meant regular treks into the far reaches of the ranch to round up enough cattle to meet our commitment.

It had rained this particular morning, so humidity made it seem hotter than usual. We'd actually had an early morning thunderstorm. Despite the sun peeking over the horizon, it was still just about dark as night. Andree Ann lit lanterns in the house as she prepared food for our venture. The rain fell with those huge swollen raindrops that splatter heavily on window panes. Sheets of rain were interspersed with jagged streaks of lightning and peals of thunder. We always worried about heavy rain, as dry creek beds could quickly fill to overflowing and flash floods become a concern. This storm was blessedly brief. In no time, the sky was pretty much clear.

Dan Carroll and Carlos Diaz joined me on this particular day. We loaded a pack mule to haul supplies, figuring we'd be out for at least a couple of days. We decided to ride along the northwest area of the ranch, as some of my other hands said they had seen a few head up that way about a week earlier. Rough weather had discouraged them from bringing the cattle in at that time.

Off we rode. We sang and carried on rather loudly. If there were any human or animal varmints out there, they'd be scared off for sure. Likely as not, we might have scared some yearlings, too. Now and then, we'd spook a family of javelina or a deer.

We had ridden quite a way when we started to track along a mostly dry creek bed. There was plenty of scrub growth along what would normally have been the banks of the creek. We didn't figure at the time that also meant plenty of cover for anyone so inclined to hide behind it. But it made sense for us to track along the creek bed. After all, I figured that beeves might come down to drink at the few remaining pools of water on their own and make our job a bit easier. Little did we know what would await us.

Well, we hadn't gone very far up that creek bed when we rounded a live oak motte and found ourselves in the middle of a Comanche ambush. They came at us from all sides, whooping and hollering like banshees. Self-preservation quickly overcame panic. Dan Carroll was quickly spared any possibility of torture, as he took three arrows to his chest. We figured there must have been at least a dozen warriors. Arrows whizzed past our heads seemingly from every possible direction. What were these savages still doing in this part of Texas and what the blazes did they want?

Diaz and I wheeled our mounts, hoping to make a break for it. By this time, my Colt 1861 Army revolver had found its way into my hand, and I shot at least one warrior off his pony. With pistol in one hand and Winchester carbine in the other, I depended on my horse to respond to knee pressure and the occasional jab of my spurs. Suddenly, I found myself face to face with none other than what appeared to be a Comanche chief. We were no more than 10 feet apart. Everything seemed to freeze. The chief had stopped as well, but his fierce stare quickly turned to a sort of knowing look. Apparently, he recognized me from the raid on my ranch. He had been that fearsome warrior that I went eyeball to eyeball with. I felt sweat oozing from every pore and the hair on the back of my neck stood straight up. Would I use my pistol on him or on myself? His hand swiftly shot up as he let out a loud short yelp, and that's when the attack halted. Diaz was now by my side, also trying to make out what was happening. In fact, this had all occurred in a space of only a few of seconds.

The chief was impressive. His bonnet featured many feathers, and the buffalo robe draped over his wide shoulders was parted enough to reveal an ornate bone breastplate over a well-muscled chest. Black war paint covered much of his face. His dark hair fell in two long braids wrapped in rust-colored fur – likely fox. He was no youngster. He'd likely seen plenty of battles, as he was every bit a warrior, every inch a chief. He was astride what was likely his very best pony, a pinto with exceptionally long mane and tail whose hide glistened in the hot humid air. It was as though man and beast were one, as the pony responded to the chief's slightest move. Despite his chiefly bearing and lean-muscled frame, I could see his ribs under the breastplate. Hunger. The Comanche were ever more desperate.

We locked eyes for what seemed like an eternity. It was as though

I were staring into two glowing black coals, and yet there was a certain sadness, even hopelessness about his eyes. Then, inexplicably, he turned his pony and galloped away. One of his band grabbed Dan Carroll's horse, others helped mount the two wounded warriors, and they all left with nary another arrow shot or bullet fired.

We breathed easier. About this time, I noticed an arrow lodged under my saddle horn. I was grateful it had missed both me and my horse. Diaz found an arrow stuck between his boot and a stirrup. We'd been incredibly lucky. It was 1877, and we possibly had just experienced what might have been the very last Comanche attack on the Nueces Strip.

Diaz and I hoisted poor Dan over the back of our mule, and we made a purposeful beeline for home. Neither of us made a sound. The earlier carefree singing and carrying on were simply inappropriate. We were grateful to our God for protecting Diaz and me.

We trotted up to the corral a little before sundown. I looked over at the house. Andree Ann and a couple of our kids were on the gallery. The look on her face said volumes. Our obviously tired, well-lathered horses and Dan's body slung over the pack mule told everything.

As we approached, I called out to Andree Ann's inquiring look. "Comanche, love. They ambushed us nearly a day out from here." I dismounted and signaled Diaz to take care of the horses and take Dan's body to the bunkhouse. Then, I turned to Andree Ann and doffed my hat.

She was relieved and upset. Her face was uncharacteristically pale. "How could you have ridden into a trap?" It didn't matter that ambushes were what Comanche did, and they were very good at it. "How could you? What if…" and she slumped into my arms.

I held her for a few moments until the sobs subsided. "It was strange, Andree Ann. Just as the attack was heating up, the chief called it off. I think it was the same band that attacked us here a while back."

We slowly walked arm in arm back into the house. My seven-year-old son John trailed along with an arrow he pulled from the mule's pack. Guess we hadn't noticed it when we placed Dan on the mule. John would have something to show off to his sister Nellie. She already had her collection of Comanche arrows, so John was intent on building his very own collection of battle trophies.

"Is this worth it, Nick?" I'd never heard Andree Ann sound any hint of doubt about our life here on the South Texas frontier. Even the Comanche attack on our ranch hadn't revealed doubt.

"Don't ever forget what we left behind in Ireland, love." I looked deep into her eyes. "We've made a life here, and it will only get better. The children love this country, and we've got plenty of family."

She pressed her head tightly against my chest and was silent for a moment. "Yes, my love, it's worth it," she sighed. It may have sounded a shade corny, but it was the truth.

The next morning, I rode to the Collins settlement – this would later become the city of Alice – and was fortunate to find a Texas Ranger. I recognized him as one of the men who'd been in Captain McNelly's company. I told him what had happened to us out on the range and how the chief had called off his warriors.

"Well, Mr. Dunn, that beats all." He scratched his grizzled chin. "I figure the chief must have recognized you from that attack on your ranch and decided you were some sort of strong medicine. That's one you'll be tellin' your grandkids."

"Is it just me, or do the Comanche seem to be ever more desperate?"

"The remaining Comanche up north have finally agreed to go on reservation. I think others sense that the end of their way of living is near. Even their friends the Kiowa have surrendered to reservation life." He swirled his coffee absentmindedly. "The damned Comanche aren't even supposed to be near here anymore, Mr. Dunn. But it's a big country an' I hear tell that more and more acreage is being carved up with fencing."

I poured a fresh cup of coffee and set down at the table in front of the Ranger. He seemed to welcome the gesture and opportunity to chat. "Well, I figure to outlast them. Besides, I'm not up to donating a red-hair scalp to their collection." That made for laughs. "You might get the word out that these Comanche are roaming around."

"I hear there's Apache trouble out in the Big Bend area near El Paso. Them Lipan Apache are joined up with the Mescaleros and Chiricahuas." The Ranger shook his head resignedly. "Wonder when we'll be done with them Redskins."

We shared coffee and made more small talk for a brief while. Nobody in these parts carried on long conversation, as you may have figured by now. Anyway, the Ranger promised to gather a few men and go out and snoop around for the Comanche band. Not that any search would amount to much, as the Comanche were surely long gone from these parts and could easily blend into the landscape if they cared to.

I headed home, mulling over the fate of the Comanche and other tribes. The ride took a while, so I had plenty of time to think. By resisting the onslaught of settlement of the frontier, the Indians were fighting a losing cause. The white man wasn't exactly treating them fairly so far as I could tell. The Comanche and their sometime Apache allies were essentially the last holdouts of an ancient civilization that was fast disappearing. While some chiefs continued to fight, the big Comanche chiefs like Buffalo Hump and the famed Quanah Parker had given in. Of course, Buffalo Hump had passed away. I got to thinking that the barbaric clashes of the aboriginal buffalo-plains horsemen with my Irish kinfolk here in South Texas might have been more appreciated by the ancient Celts, whose atrocities rivaled the Comanche.

By the time I reached the ranch, I had turned my thoughts back around to the next cattle drive and sale of our beef back in Corpus Christi. It was pretty dark by the time I got Thunder in his stall and cooled him down. Andree Ann had whipped up a fine dinner, and the kids all wanted to hug me at once. I must admit, I was feeling mighty legendary to my family.

TWELVE

Posses, Rangers, & Militia

Never squat with your spurs on.

Texas-ism

The post-Reconstruction 1870s featured downright nasty weather with drought followed by an unusually cold winter. Cattle died by the thousands for lack of food and water. Cowboys found themselves out of work. Virtually any man with a knife became what they called a hider, looking for dead cattle to skin for their valuable hides. Some ranchers actually hired hiders and shared the earnings.

Not all hiders were honest. With the end of the War Between the States, banditos from Mexico habitually stole cattle for the hides. Given the dropping price of beef, it turned out that the hides were worth more than the meat. These greedy banditos operated in gangs of up to 100 men, and killed thousands, even skinning some while still alive. The killing was likened to the slaughter of the buffalo. Two of the best-known hider banditos were Pat Quinn and Alberto Garza. These ne'er-do-wells were linked to the Mexican bandit leader General Juan "Cheno" Cortina, whom I mentioned earlier.

The Texas Rangers were called in to bring an end to what was called by some the Skinning War. They were to deliver justice, even if it meant decorating live oak and mesquite branches around the region with bandito-filled nooses. It was sort of God's wrath at work. I expect for many people such lynchings come across as an ugly – maybe even disgusting – image, but reality can be tough. Texans have never taken kindly to folks messing around illegally with livestock, be it horses or cattle, no matter the circumstances. I can't say as I'd be especially anxious to hang a man without a fair trial, but neither am I going to sit in judgment of some ranchers who might resort to hanging offenders caught in the act of committing their crimes.

We Dunns didn't confine ourselves to farming and trading in livestock. Our apparent destiny in South Texas went well beyond that. I vividly remember the wildly diverse exploits of my cousin, John Beamond "Red John" Dunn. He was the oldest of my Uncle Matt's three sons. You may recall "Red John's" battle with yellow fever, as I described earlier in my story. "Red John" is an integral part of Dunn family lore, though he was hardly a paragon of virtue. One could say he was the gray sheep of the family, to put it kindly. In his early days, it was said that he was a drover moving cattle to Kansas, fired boilers on a Mississippi River steamer, worked in livestock slaughterhouses, and raised a few head of cattle himself. Of course, there's more... much more.

Virtually every history of South Texas describes the Good Friday Raid on March 26, 1875. It's part of the Dunn story, part of my story. I deeply regretted at the time that I wasn't personally there to help, as I was engaged in some cattle business up north near Victoria and thus was far removed from the action. Even had I been at home, it would have been nearly a day's ride to get to the scene of the raid. So what I will relate was what I learned immediately following the raid from my father, brothers, and cousins who participated in the legendary event. The Good Friday Raid stands as testament to the resilience and fighting spirit of the settlers of South Texas and especially the Dunn family.

Keep in mind that Texas around this time was quite thinly populated, even around Corpus Christi environs. It was fair to assume that longhorns and horses far outnumbered humans. There might be 40 or even 50 miles between homesteads or settlements, especially the Comancheria west of the 98th meridian. While most everyone was armed, there was plenty of open space for Indians or desperadoes to roam and lots of cover in which to lurk. A good-bye kiss to a loved one in the morning could be your last.

Apparently, several bands of what they called river bandits were swarming up through Duval County and Bee County and were heading toward Goliad and Refugio. They raided the King Ranch twice, though that might not have been their wisest tactic despite the vast range and thousands of head of livestock. The bandits were thought to be part of a group originally brought together by revolutionary rabble-rouser Juan Cortina in Mexico. Notably, Cortina really wasn't much of a factor anymore, as he'd been arrested in Mexico owing to his revolutionary tendencies and was being held under house arrest. Vigilantes were delaying the thieves, but not so much as needed. As these particular bandits advanced northward through the Nueces Strip toward the Nueces River, they harassed or murdered nearly all who crossed their path or had the temerity to resist.

Texas Ranger Captain Leander McNelly, whom I'd dealt with previously, had been determined to bring them to justice before his illness would bring him to an untimely end. McNelly was apparently incensed that the bandit gang had the temerity to have stolen 18 brand-new Dick Heyes saddles. These saddles were just about the fanciest, most expensive saddles to be had. Stealing a Dick Heyes saddle was tantamount to earning a death warrant. The Texas Rangers were said to have ordered any bandit found riding one of those saddles to be shot off of it. Care was to be taken not to damage the saddles. As I'll describe shortly, the Texas Ranger methods of dealing with the saddle thieves were nothing if not highly effective. By the way, my brother Mike was credited with giving McNelly an accurate description of those saddles. As a horseman of considerable repute, Mike seemed to appreciate fancy saddles as much as fine horse flesh.

The Good Friday Raid episode of Texas history began when this particular band of Cortina's heavily armed cutthroats stopped near Nuecestown about 13 miles northwest of Corpus Christi. They took a group of 11 prominent citizenry hostage and headed up the main road toward Corpus Christi. A fellow named Jim Hunter accidentally came upon them and was fortunate enough to avoid capture. He rode at breakneck speed up the road to warn the citizens of the city. He arrived on his heavily lathered horse, hollering for the residents to prepare to defend the city. In turn, the residents immediately held a town hall meeting to figure how to protect Corpus Christi. Partly as a consequence of port war policies, the citizens were short on arms and ammunition. They set up a defensive perimeter up the road toward where they figured the bandits would likely approach. Some of the female residents even boarded boats to wait out any attack offshore in Corpus Christi Bay. They sat out on the waters of the bay for quite a while with naught but tiny parasols as protection from the sun and a few blankets as shields from the chilly March weather.

Meanwhile, the raiders camped nearby and apparently amused themselves by forcing their captives to perform embarrassing dances. Fortunately, the women were eventually freed, likely as they were going to slow the raiders' travels. The next day, the raiders made their way to Nuecestown proper with their remaining captives. Nuecestown had been founded a couple of decades earlier by Colonel Kinney, as its location lent itself to establishing a ferry across the Nueces River. It was not the fastest growing town on the Nueces Strip, but was underdefended and did make an attractive enough target for the bandit gang.

They terrorized local merchant Thomas Noakes and his wife before looting and burning their store. They as likely stole a few Noakes saddles because they were nearly as prized as the Dick Heyes saddles they had already acquired. At least, Noakes had managed to dispatch one of the raiders with a shot to the chest, though a man known as "Lying" Smith subsequently rushed from the shelter of the store and was shot and killed by the raiders. For their part, I heard the bandits were a bit high on whiskey.

On Good Friday proper, my brother Mike and his family were returning from a short visit west of their home, and they drove their rig right into a bunch of those same Mexican bandits sweeping along the countryside, now about 10 miles west of Corpus Christi. The raiders – some seated on those newly-acquired Dick Heyes and Noakes saddles – quickly rounded up their mostly unarmed prey. Along with the other captives, Mike was driven up the old Nuecestown Road in a trot on foot ahead of the raiders. It was scary and frightening. Knowing Mike, he was alert and itching to find a way to escape.

Meanwhile, my father John was at home preparing to head off to town to attend Good Friday services when he was notified of the raid and kidnapping by a small boy driving by in a wagon. My father quickly wrote a note for the boy to deliver to Nueces County Sheriff John McClane, grabbed a couple of extra rifles, began loading his cap and ball pistol, and mounted his horse to head toward Corpus Christi to possibly intercept the kidnappers. With my cousins "Red John" Dunn and Pat Dunn joining him, he sped toward the scene of the incident. My father may no longer have been a young man, but he had plenty of feisty Irish blood running in his veins, made heartier by tough Texas living.

When the small band of men discovered the raiders near Nuecestown, they immediately found that they were far outnumbered by them and in need of assistance, which they had been expecting to arrive at any moment. My father, at the insistence of the others, sped back to town for help. According to his own account, he found the town armed and Sheriff McClane riding through the streets urging the citizens to protect themselves against a horde of Mexicans whom he thought were poised to attack the city. McClane was not inclined to pursue the bandits, believing that his place was with the townspeople.

My father was able to recruit only a handful of men and, brushing the sheriff aside, rode with them to join the small posse back along the Nuecestown Road. Gathered just out of range of the heavily-armed Mexican raiders were my father, "Red John," James, Patrick, and George Dunn; Clem Vetters; Pat Whelan; Washington "Wash" Mussett; Bass Burrows; Jesus Seguira; and George Swanks. The leadership of the posse has generally been credited to Pat Whelan, though it was the Dunn family that mostly pulled it together. So far as the men of the posse could tell, the Mexicans didn't yet know they'd been discovered. As the kidnappers moved on, the posse followed them at a safe distance. The raiders had a wagon that was presumed to contain their prisoners. Of course, the posse was blessed that the wagon tended to slow the bandits' progress.

Growing ever more impatient, Swanks finally had had enough. In a seething fit of anger, he grew recklessly impatient and, riding a fast horse and letting loose with a fierce cowboy yell, charged into the raiders. At first, the surprised raiders beat a hasty retreat, but one of them managed to get off a shot that killed Swanks, who immediately fell from his mount. The posse had tried to stop him, but to no avail. Any element of surprise was now lost. There was nothing left to do but attack. "Red John" started everyone into shooting and yelling Comanche whoops and Texas yells, then led the group in a charge that caused the raiders to likely think that all of Corpus Christi was upon them. The way "Red John" later described it, the ends of some of the posse members' cartridges had been split such that, when fired, they made a hideous wailing sound. As if to amplify the woes of those river bandits, "Red John" had a single-shot, .50-caliber Sharps carbine – better known for its effectiveness in killing buffalo. It had a tremendous recoil, but no raider could hope to survive a hit by a slug fired from that Sharps. The raiders leaped to their mounts and got away as quickly as they could. Mike and the other prisoners were freed. By God's grace and the posse's bravery, all were unharmed. George Swanks had been the only soul lost that day. We did dispatch a couple of the raiders and surely wounded some of the others. The attack only lasted a few minutes and, in the heat of battle, no one was keeping track of bandit casualties.

As I heard tell, it was certainly a good thing the raiders took off. My father and the rest of the posse had nearly run out of ammunition. They could have become easy pickings for those Mexican thieves.

The posse retrieved Swanks' body and used the horses recovered from the banditos to ease transport of the freed prisoners back to Corpus Christi. Everyone was cheered as they entered the city. The women out on the bay were relieved to get back to shore, though their situation hadn't come close to being comparable to what was endured by my family and the other hostages. Sheriff McClane was oddly resentful of the resounding success of the posse and meekly thanked them for their service to Corpus Christi. My father and the others wouldn't soon forget the affront. Folks, sheriffs included, generally didn't mess with Dunns.

Most of those stolen saddles were eventually recovered, though there was no exact accounting of how many banditos riding Dick Heyes or Noakes saddles were killed in the ensuing months. One of the Mexican raiders from the battle was captured by a posse organized by Sheriff McClane, but about four days later was taken by an angry mob and lynched. McClane had been forced to take action, given how embarrassed he was about not helping free the hostages.

The residents of the Nueces Strip retaliated against the raiders with a vengeance, organizing militia or vigilance committees in every county from the Nueces River to the Rio Grande. These vigilante-style militia proceeded to hunt down and mete out justice to Mexican outlaws, but regrettably also looted property and burned homes of peaceful citizens. They especially exacted revenge on Mexicans with new saddles, Noakes, Dick Heyes, or otherwise. Regrettably, some of those saddles were likely purchased legitimately. It wasn't right, but that was the way it was.

I expect I lost a few cattle from the ranch during this period, thanks to rustlers inspired by Cortina. It was hard to keep an accurate count. It was likely a blessing that Richard King's ranch to the south of me with his armed *vaqueros* served as a bit of a southern buffer from mine and several other spreads.

I wish I could say these tales were exaggerations, but this part of Texas was very much the wild west and these sorts of events were all too common. As though Mexican banditos weren't enough, neither were the Comanche quite finished. They were a proud people, unable to adapt to the inevitable change happening before their very eyes. South Texas was mostly beyond what was considered Comancheria, but Comanche knew no boundaries.

The U.S. Cavalry hunted them relentlessly, and the Comanche were growing ever more desperate. To add to their plight, buffalo hunters had begun to show up in ever greater numbers in response to the demand for hides in key markets like San Antonio, Corpus Christi, and New Orleans. They would eventually pretty much wipe out these beasts of the plains.

The Comanche turned to rustling horses and cattle, which was a poor substitute for the dwindling buffalo. Raiding cattle ranches became a sort of last gasp of the proud Comanche. Most of their activities were confined to the Texas Panhandle, so we needed not worry so much down on the Nueces Strip. Unlike the Apache that rustled and traded beeves for profit while preserving the ranches and settlers as sources of future livestock raids, the Comanche still exercised their ruthless habits of killing, kidnapping, and torturing victims. Pressure was building to bring an end to the Comanche threat once and for all.

The history of Indian fighting around the Nueces Strip tells of a dwindling but still dangerous environment. I've shared some of my own violent encounters. The demise of the Indian way of life seemed inevitable. While the Comanche were declining, the Lipan Apache under their chief Costalites still marauded throughout the Nueces Strip with impunity. Costalites had made several alliances, including the one with Comanche Chief Také-vera, in an attempt to defend against increasingly aggressive attacks by the Mexican Army. Eventually, in 1873, Colonel Ranald MacKenzie and six companies of the U.S. 4th Cavalry crossed the Rio Grande into Mexico and attacked Costalites' camp, as well as a Kickapoo tribal camp at El Remolino and another Lipan Apache village. They killed 19 Apache and took 41 prisoners, including Costalites. The Apache chief managed to escape and would be found dead near San Antonio a few days later. The remaining Lipan Apaches were deported to the Mescalero Apache Reservation in New Mexico.

The newly reconstituted Texas Rangers were called in to support the efforts begun by the U.S. Cavalry, which had – after disposing of Costalites' band – moved northward to take on a handful of doggedly determined Comanche tribes. This relocation of U.S. Cavalry was an ongoing cause of consternation among us Texans on the Nueces Strip.

I learned that my cousin "Red John" joined up with a local Texas Ranger company of roughly 60 men under a fellow named Bland Chamberlain. As I've mentioned, the Rangers were a diverse lot and some were of doubtful morals. The Ranger culture had necessarily changed since the time of legendary Captain Leander McNelly. Chamberlain's troop consisted of only five Texans; the rest came from Mexico, Louisiana, and other locales. In "Red John's" company, at least one man – Gus Pool – had served with the infamous Quantrill's Raiders during the War Between the States, and several others had less-than-reputable histories. While Ranger troops may have seemed to some to be a bit ragtag appearance-wise, they were as effective a fighting force against hostile Indians and Mexican bandits as could be assembled. After all, many of them had nothing to lose. Unsurprisingly, Ranger methods – inclusive of vigilante-style lynching – were often outside the law. They didn't see so many Comanche or Apache, but cleared numerous Mexican banditos and other lawbreakers from the Nueces Strip.

"Red John" soon left Chamberlain's troop, which was disbanded after about nine months, owing to their poor behavior. My cousin joined up with a new Texas Ranger battalion headquartered in Duval County under Warren Wallace. The Mexican-Americans called these Rangers *rinches* (rangers), and it was this battalion, along with implementing the heavy-handed, take-no-prisoners approach made famous by Captain McNelly, that gave the Rangers a bad name in the region and caused a lot of consternation back in Austin. "Red John" was supposedly involved in the brutal lynching of a fellow they called Moss Top; later was linked with the murder of the manager of a Mexican circus; and then was involved in the attack on a couple of Mexican shepherds as they cooked their meal. Additional atrocities led to the eventual disbanding of Wallace's battalion. Of note by this time, "Red John" had traded in his old but powerful and trusty Sharps rifle for a Winchester 1873 repeating rifle – known generally as the rifle that won the west.

The often-unjust deeds of "Red John" and others eventually caught up with them. They were tried for robbery and murder at a court in San Patricio. I sat in at the trial and can't say as I heard convincing arguments one way or the other. I felt it my duty to support my family, though I likely felt a bit of guilt at having missed joining the posse during that Good Friday Raid back in 1875. "Red John" was acquitted under what seemed to me to be vague circumstances that I didn't fully comprehend and won't attempt to describe here. Partly as a consequence of the trial, there was a resulting general perception along the Nueces Strip that any killing of Mexicans wasn't a punishable crime. So far as my dear cousin "Red John," it was little wonder that he became known as the "black sheep" of the Dunn family in South Texas, thanks to those exploits with the Texas Rangers and later escapades as a vigilante. I use the term vigilante a bit loosely here, as he headed a group more closely resembling a bandit gang. Despite his character flaws, "Red John" certainly was Texan to the bone in terms of swagger.

At the risk of repeating myself, I feel compelled to add just a bit more about Texas Ranger Captain Leander McNelly, given his contribution to the taming of the Nueces Strip. McNelly was a no-nonsense Texas Ranger in the stripe of Rangers like John Salmon "Rip" Ford and John Coffee Hays. He earned notoriety for having the guts to pursue lawbreakers south into the very bowels of Mexico. He counted on U.S. troops being ready and able to cover his backside from the Texas side of the Rio Grande. But such support wasn't assured. One time, upon not receiving support from U.S. troops in his vigorous pursuit of Mexican cattle thieves into Mexico, McNelly purportedly penned a note, "I shall remain in Mexico with my Rangers and cross back at my discretion. Give my compliments to the Secretary of War and tell him and his United States soldiers to go to hell." At least, that's what I heard. After exacting retribution from the Mexicans in the form of return of some of the stolen cattle, McNelly re-crossed the Rio Grande and turned his attention northward to take on domestic criminals on the Nueces Strip like the previously mentioned strongman King Fisher.

My fascinating cousin "Red John" wasn't finished with his adventures, however, and joined a band of militia riders – vigilantes in common parlance – that was led by a cattleman from Banquette named T. Hines Clark and included my cousin Matt Dunn. In my humble view and as I've already implied, they seemed more like an outlaw gang than any civilian militia. This group took to vigilante activities, especially pursuing hiders – those who rustled and killed cattle only for the hides. They burned several of what were called Mexican ranches. They weren't ranches in the classic sense, but more clusters of houses where hide trading would occur. Many a thief wound up sporting a hemp neck-tie and hanging lonely-like from the branches of a live oak tree. All of this resulted in blood feuds that lasted years afterward.

"Red John" even had a near run-in with the notorious murderer John Wesley Hardin and wrote about witnessing Hardin killing a man and wounding another. As to "Red John's" view of all this, I never figured out his conscience nor sensed any feelings of guilt over his deeds, though I think he truly enjoyed the adventure and personal sense of justice, misplaced or not. On the couple of occasions when "Red John" and I discussed our widely disparate lifestyles – held together by a common family bond, mind you – I got the sense that he deeply respected me for my devotion to family and business. He knew from family stories about my bold engagements with Comanche that I was not someone that would back away from a fight. I vividly picture "Red John" – at this time in his mid-thirties – smiling mischievously through his bright red handlebar mustache while his mind raced to recollect and tell tales of his encounters with lawbreakers. Of course, he naturally attracted the male Dunn children, who were drawn in by his gripping, colorful, and often exaggerated storytelling. He as likely inherited his story spinning abilities from our common ancestor, Long Larry Dunn. "Red John" could spin the very best Irish blarney.

Meanwhile, new Ranger companies were being formed up, while the U.S. Cavalry remained focused on the few remaining Indians. I heard that the government was disposing of the Indians to make way for the transcontinental railroads. Apparently, the "scorched-earth" tactics employed by Union generals during the War Between the States were being applied to fighting the Sioux and other tribes further northward, as entire villages including women, children, and the elderly were quite literally wiped out. The Comanche were no exception. It was sad, but I figured both sides had trouble with keeping promises. I always reminded myself that the name Comanche loosely translated to "enemy." They were pretty much everyone's enemy, and their treatment of prisoners didn't endear them to the good settlers of Texas.

Most of the few remaining Comanche chiefs were eventually persuaded to pow-wow and move to reservations in Oklahoma Territory. The Comanche were among the last of the major southwestern tribes to sue for peace. Famed half-breed chief Quanah Parker of the Quahadi Comanche, a ruthless, clever, and fearless leader, would be the last of his tribe to surrender to the reservation life. Even Quanah came to recognize that, with the demise of the buffalo and the ravages of "white man's diseases," his days on the open prairies were numbered.

My dear cousin "Red John" Dunn soon gave up his wildly adventurous ways. He went on to engage in a bit of farming, became a dairyman, and married Lelia Nias. They were blessed with four children: Georgia, John, Lelia, and Mary Maude. "Red John" dabbled in the hotel business (opened the Crescent Hotel in Corpus Christi) and eventually opened an impressive private museum of military relics and memorabilia on Shell Road near Corpus Christi. Doggone, but "Red John" had apparently been collecting his museum pieces beginning from the age of seventeen. He surely embodied much of the rough-and-tumble life and legend of the old west –especially South Texas. It would be fair to say that "Red John" was one of the most notorious Dunn family members. If he wasn't that "black sheep" of the family, he was the "gray sheep," for sure.

To those following my story, this all likely sounds pretty exciting. But a sort of normal life counterbalanced Indian raids, thievery, politics, and the like. It'd be easy to boast of my own exploits and those of my family, but I was never aiming to be fodder for dimestore novels.

They'd have exaggerated a reality that needed no embellishment.

By this time, Corpus Christi had become a serious port for shipping cattle. It made for a convenient alternative to the long drives northward. As I've mentioned, I was typically shipping upward of 100 or more head of beef a week by steamer to New Orleans. As a humorous aside, I heard that some folks – the type that would sound a sour note in a choir full of jackasses – took issue with my naming bulls and stallions and not giving names to cows and mares. As I think back, I guess that was true. Petty, certainly, but true. Can't say as to why. We owned lots of trouble-making cows and bulls that could have earned names, but we mostly stuck to naming horses for breeding purposes with designations per the color of the stallion. We called the herds *manadas* or bunches. *Manada* is Spanish for a herd of common breed. We kept track of how many fillies and how many horses in the brown horse *manada*, the sorrel *manada*, the bay *manada*, the black horse *manada*, and so on. But a beef was mostly simply a beef.

We were a diverse and self-reliant lot. Whether ranching, tilling, blacksmithing, law enforcing, railroad building, grocery selling, whatever Dunns undertook was usually successful.

THIRTEEN

Texan Family to the Core

Sweeter than stolen honey.
Texas-ism

It may seem a bit old-fashioned, even quaint, to city folk, but here were Andree Ann and I ensconced on a swing on the gallery of our home overlooking the ranch spread out before us as far as the eye could see. We were enjoying a warm breeze and crystal blue sky with a few wispy clouds off in the distance. There's really nothing to compare with a big blue Texas sky. There were some live oak and a few lonely mesquite to break the view. We'd been blessed with six surviving children thus far, and Andree Ann was expecting another in a couple of months. For the moment, it was hard to believe that we still lived close to the fringe of the frontier.

"John!" I called out firmly. "Lad, be kind to your sister." He'd just put a toad down the back of Mary's shirt. I sort of chuckled inside as I thought back to how I'd tortured my own sister Annie with dead rattlesnakes.

Little Maggie, age 2½, sat at Andree Ann's feet toying with a ball of pink yarn. The other end was attached to a blanket Andree Ann was knitting for the anticipated birth. I thought pink was a bit presumptuous, as we had no way of knowing whether we'd have son or daughter. But women have a way of knowing these things. Go figure. Andree Ann had already chosen her name: Teresa.

"Nick, we don't do this nearly enough." She was referring to our taking some time just to be together as a family. Except for occasionally getting to church or a family gathering, we didn't do as much as we should as a family.

She was right, of course. Too often, I found myself away checking our livestock across our 15,000-acre spread or making deals in Corpus Christi or San Antonio for our next cattle sale or purchase.

"John especially misses you." She nailed that truth. It was only in the past couple of weeks that I'd taken John with me to Corpus Christi to buy cattle. He was so proud to join me, and I had to admit that he sat a horse quite well for a 7-year-old. But for his youthful appearance and not yet being full grown, he might have passed for a livestock speculator in terms of the confident style he was inclined to project. Shucks, I think his hat was nearly as big as he was. I had a feeling that he had his great grandfather Long Larry's blood in him and would grow to be a tall drink of water and just as tough.

"This is the life, isn't it, my love?" Both our families had immigrated to America – to Texas – to make a better life. "Do you ever think of us visiting the old country?"

To be fair, Andree Ann was born in South Texas. Her parents had immigrated before she was born, though her father had passed away while she was very young. Given that I'd spent 15 years of my life growing up in County Kildare, she didn't have the Irish history as I had. "In a way," and she gazed off into the vast azure sky. "Do you wonder whether you'll ever see Kildare again?" I pondered her question, lost for the moment in thoughts of Ireland.

"John, put the toad down!" Distractions. "Mary doesn't want to eat the toad." These toads were fearsome looking little creatures covered with all sorts of what looked like horns. We'd taken to calling them horny toads. I turned back to Andree Ann. For a brief moment, I felt a wee bit of a catch in my throat. I knew it was highly unlikely that I'd ever see my dear Ireland again. By now, all five of Long Larry's sons – my father and my four uncles – had settled in South Texas. "I doubt I'll see the clan again. I think we knew that when we left." I pondered the profound reality of what I'd admitted. That departure now seemed so long past. Then I added wistfully, "I do miss the heather, the lush rolling hills and forests." With Long Larry having passed away more than 20 years ago and my grandmother Ellen not long after, there really wasn't much reason to go back to visit.

About this time, John had tired of playing with the horny toad and joined Mary and Maggie on the steps to the gallery. He looked up at me with a mischievous look, "Father, please tell us again about the Comanche?" He gleefully watched expressions of concern cross Maggie's and Mary's faces.

I shook my head. "Methinks now is not quite the time, son. How about going to the barn and brushing the gray?" Andree Ann nodded approvingly. "Perhaps you could show Mary and little Maggie how it's done." Hopefully, a purposeful task would divert my energetic son from his taunting inclinations. He was a natural with livestock, but I could see more in his future. We Dunns were always stretching our limits with our business interests. For example, I'd heard that my cousin John Hillard Dunn had started dreaming of railroads, cousin "Red John" was starting to settle down to farming, and cousin Patrick Dunn was getting into raising longhorns on North Padre Island off the coast of Corpus Christi.

As the children ran off to the barn, I turned thoughtfully to Andree Ann. "I think it's time John had a horse of his own."

"I was beginning to wonder if you'd ever think of that, my love."

"I think the gray gelding would be the right choice. John can just about throw a saddle over its back when he uses a stool." I paused. "Do you agree?"

Andree Ann nodded. "You know horses and you know your son. I agree that it's a good fit."

Settled. I eased back as Andree Ann stopped her knitting and lay her head on my shoulder.

She looked up at me. "You don't ever think we'll see Comanche again, do you?"

For a moment, I felt a bit of a chill. It really hadn't been that long ago that the savages had raided our ranch. "I think they're done." I responded softly. "We likely have more to fear from rustlers."

Andree Ann settled more closely. "Then, I guess it's best that we keep the rifles where they are?" I deeply appreciated that we could talk of these things, and I valued her opinions.

I could tell that she was thinking of our youngest, Mary and Maggie. We'd lost Nellie to illness a couple of years back. Life could be hard, and death could make it harder still. We were blessed to have our strong faith to see us through such tragic events. Just as I'd done with Nellie, I'd already been teaching John and Mary to shoot and Maggie would soon be big enough to join them. In fact, Mary was getting pretty good. I made a mental note to take her hunting the next time I went out with John. "I know it's a worry, my sweet. I think we have the rifles setting high enough as to be out of the young 'uns reach."

"I love you."

I tightened my arm around her shoulder. I missed our occasional horseback rides...just the two of us. "Perhaps tomorrow we could hitch the wagon and go over to visit my folks." I figured that a family wagon ride would have to do for now.

It'd take the better part of a day to make the trip. The children would love it.

"I'm not so sure," Andree Ann offered meekly. "I've got a feeling that I've miscounted my due date."

I swallowed hard. "Perhaps I ought to be fetching Katherine." Katherine was my brother Michael's wife. She was also pregnant, but not nearly so far along.

"Aye, I don't think it will be much longer."

John soon returned from brushing the gray. "Did Maggie and Mary get to help?" I had a good feeling about asking the question. Around a working ranch, you had to grow up sooner than most places. Taking responsibility was a big part of the process.

"Yes, father...yes, they did." His siblings shrugged and nodded assent.

"So, tell me, son," I stared full into his eyes. "What do you think of the gray?"

"It's a nice mount for its size, Father." That was an honest answer, as it was a middling sized steed of nearly 15 hands at the withers. He pondered a moment, mimicking my stance when I'd bid on cattle or horses. He was a bit tall for his age, but the confident pose seemed to cast him as far more grown up. He even tilted his hat a bit, rakishly mimicking my style. "Yes, I like the gray. It's a good piece of horseflesh."

"Would you like to have it as your own?"

His eyes grew wide in joyful amazement. "Really? Mine...to own?"

"Yes...and to care for. It'll be all yours." My, but it was wonderful to feel my son's spirit lift. "I'll even throw in the tack." Of course, that was a given.

Andree Ann was smiling that same smile from when we'd first met.

This moment of family happiness was broken by the sound of horses. Reality set over our loving family tryst. Keep in mind that this was still frontier. I reflexively separated from Andree Ann and eased the Colt from its holster. I motioned to John to fetch a rifle. We held our collective breaths as five riders emerged from the far side of the barn. It was unusual to approach from that direction.

The lead rider called out as the horses slowed. "Nick...Nick Dunn?"

Texas Rangers. I eased my pistol back into its holster. "Captain Wallace?" It was "Red John's" former Ranger captain. Naturally, it was hardly a surprise that he'd show up, as the Nueces Strip was still very much alive with desperadoes intent on all manner of mayhem.

As they pulled up in front of our gallery, Andree Ann arose and paused before heading toward the door. "Y'all care for some coffee?"

"Thanks, Mrs. Dunn, but we won't be staying long enough." He cast a serious gaze at me. "Just came by to give you a heads up that some hiders have been in the area. They come up through Matamoros and Brownsville. Been asking about where the best ranches are. I think they're part of that old Juan-Cortina-inspired gang. They'll be giving the King Ranch a wide berth, and that could put folks like you in their sights."

I thought about the roughly 2,000 head that grazed our ranch. "Captain, I appreciate the warning. We'll stay on guard." I glanced at John, now standing at ease with the rifle. "I think we've got some strong folk here." John puffed out his chest just a bit and squared his jaw so as to look tough. "We'll be okay." I had three of my hired *vaqueros* and their families staying in the ranch outbuildings, and they were fiercely loyal to me. The Dunn family wouldn't be alone against any rustlers.

By this time, Andree Ann emerged with a pot of coffee – it was brewing nearly constantly these days – and a tray of tin cups. Coffee was second nature to Texans regardless of ethnic background, and everyone learned to have brewed coffee at the ready. As if on cue, a gentle breeze came up, and the tempting aroma wafted out toward the men. It was irresistible.

The Rangers dismounted. "Thank you, Mrs. Dunn. We're much obliged." It didn't take much arm twisting to get these rough men to savor some coffee. Actually, Andree Ann had developed a way of roasting and grinding the beans that drew out the full flavor when brewed.

"How do you think the road is between here and Corpus?" I was concerned lest I be unable to fetch my sister-in-law.

"We think they're southwest of here. As I said, they seem to be avoiding the King Ranch." Then he nodded toward Andree Ann. "But you can never be certain."

I chewed on that information. The King Ranch was already 50 or so times the size of my 15,000-acre spread. I had to believe they'd be protected by their own "army" of guards and cowboys. "The rustlers would be crazy to tackle the King Ranch." It was as much question as statement.

"Shucks, Nick, anybody trying to rustle cattle from any ranch in these parts nowadays has to be nuts. With the Comanche and Apache finished and King Fisher's mob under control, we can concentrate on those banditos from Mexico." He sort of hissed the word "banditos" through clenched teeth. Perhaps it's worth sharing that we purposely referred to these Mexican raiders as banditos rather than bandits. This was meant to show disrespect for them by essentially referring to them as "little bandits." Truth be told, their bullets could kill or maim as well as anyone's. Also, it wouldn't be long before barbed wire would become a serious challenge to rustlers.

The lingering danger served to keep everyone on alert. We could never fully relax. It was, after all, still a frontier.

FOURTEEN

Peace of Sorts

If I felt any better, I'd drop my harp plumb through the cloud.

Texas-ism

It seemed for the present that peace had settled over the Dunn family on the Nueces Strip. Comanche raids were definitely a thing of the past. In fact, I learned that famed Comanche Chief Quanah Parker was even charging fees to drovers for crossing over or resting herds on his reservation lands on their way to driving their beeves to railheads in Kansas. The primary disruptors of the peace remained the occasional marauding banditos that would cross the Rio Grande and make trouble with their thieving, rustling, hiding, and other mayhem. So peace is a relative term for my story.

Corpus Christi continued to thrive after the War Between the States, and Irish immigrant families held a tight grip on much of the social and economic scene. There was even an area dubbed "Irishtown," and within its bounds could be found merchants, judges, attorneys, doctors, and the like who'd found their ways from Ireland. My brother John served on the Shamrock Hose Company, a local firefighting unit.

My father and brother even helped found St. Patrick's in Corpus Christi. It made sense, given my father's strong faith and concern for the influence of the church. He was especially concerned with education and donated property in support of Father Bernard O'Reilly's efforts to establish schools.

By way of refreshing your memory and offering up some context so far as bringing justice to the region, keep in mind that, with Texas having been readmitted to the Union in 1870, there had been a move afoot back then to officially reconstitute the Texas Rangers. Under the administration of Reconstructionist Governor E.J. Davis, the Texas Rangers had been broken up, reorganized as the State Police, and charged with enforcing the wildly unpopular carpetbagger laws. Most units were made up of Negroes – former slaves – who were none too easy on Anglo Texans. In fact, they could be downright nasty, though I never directly encountered them. Most of us still called them Rangers, but such were the vagaries of government under Reconstruction. Can't say as Andree Ann and I found these times to our liking. With the end of those laws in 1873, new Governor Richard Coke organized six companies of Texas Rangers. These 75-man companies were stationed at strategic points around Texas to be on hand to respond when ranches were raided, towns were threatened, or citizens were in need of protection. As peace officers – as opposed to being semi-military – they were charged with not only confronting any remaining hostile Indians or Mexicans, but dealing with society's misfits in the form of outlaws, rustlers, train robbers, and such. It remained tough duty for those who chose to put on the star. So here we were, roughly ten years later, and a peace of sorts had indeed settled over the South Texas region.

Also recall, as I previously shared, my cousin "Red John" served as a Texas Ranger in one of those newly formed companies. I may be prejudiced, but I think he was a fine Ranger and – despite his violent inclinations – was typical of the majority who strove to uphold the law to the best of their abilities in what were still brutally rough territories. From my own forays out on the open range of my ranch for a couple of days at a time, it takes little imagination to fully appreciate living extended days on horseback while never knowing what lurked around the next bend in the trail.

I would be remiss if I did not share a bit of the life of my dear cousin Patrick Dunn, born in 1858 and one of nine children of my Uncle Thomas. Patrick's teen years were spent working with cattle on the open range, but the advent of barbed wire in 1884 eventually forced smaller ranchers he worked with to move elsewhere or go out of business. Barbed wire, mind you, had been invented back in the 1860s, but only began to be seriously applied in Texas in the mid-1880s. It defined property lines and often protected all-important water access. At age 21, Patrick partnered with his brother Thomas, Jr. to establish a ranch on Padre Island, located just southeast of Corpus Christi. Bordered as it was on all sides by water, Padre Island had the advantage of needing very little fencing. Other advantages were that very little brush grew on the island, thus making it easier to keep an eye on cattle, and drinking water was plentiful and could be easily accessed through shallow fresh water wells (Patrick dug 75 wells). Between leasing part of the island and purchasing his own cattle, Patrick managed to populate the island with more than 1,000 head. He built three line-camps at 15-mile intervals. Each camp was comprised of a bunkhouse for the *vaqueros*, a small bunkhouse for Patrick, an outdoor kitchen, and various cattle traps. Cattle were rounded up in May and October for branding and selection of yearlings for market. It would take about three weeks to round up beeves and drive them north to be herded across Laguna Madre for sale in Corpus Christi. Patrick soon became known as the Duke of Padre Island. He, his wife Clara, and their three children actually lived nearby in Corpus Christi before eventually moving to a small settlement on the island. They built a beautiful home, much of it constructed of fine mahogany from furniture washed ashore from shipwrecks. On more than one occasion,

I gathered Andree Ann and the children and made the trip to Patrick's ranch – with a stop in Corpus Christi, of course, for a bit of shopping. The sand, sea air, and warm gulf waters of the island were a stark contrast to our ranch, and we loved the respite from the dusty prairies. Naturally, Patrick and I would share our ranching experiences, and I would occasionally help him with buying and selling his stock.

As I tell my story – and my family's story – in these pages, I'm struck by the fact that I'm pushing well past 45 years old. Since coming to Texas, I have to admit that I've packed a lot into those more than three decades of building a life here. Many would say I'm in the prime of life. Andree Ann – the love of my life – and I have five bright and alive children, and we're raising them on a large thriving ranch offering all manner of wonderful life experiences. God blessed us with His bounty. Andree Ann still has that beautiful smile that had won my heart back at church nearly two decades ago. While my son John was becoming the mirror image of me in terms of an adventurous, life-loving, competitive yet practical spirit, I have to admit partiality to my four dear daughters. I am fiercely protective of them. Pity any man who would even try to hurt one of my girls.

While I try to be a good man and practicing Catholic, I have never been what you might call religious. That being said, my mother used to bring my attention to the Bible on a regular basis. One set of verses especially stood out, and I strove to incorporate them in my family so far as possible. Ephesians 5:21 tells us to submit to one another in the name of Christ, and then in verses 22 to 30 it further says, "*Wives, submit to your own husbands as to the Lord, for the husband is the head of the wife as Christ is the head of the church. He is the Savior of the body. Now as the church submits to Christ, so wives are to submit to their husbands in everything. Husbands, love your wives, just as Christ loved the church and gave Himself for her to make her holy, cleansing her with the washing of water by the word. He did this to present the church to Himself in splendor, without spot or wrinkle or anything like that, but holy and blameless. In the same way, husbands are to love their wives as their own bodies. He who loves his wife loves himself. For no one ever hates his own flesh but provides and cares for it, just as Christ does for the church, since we are members of His body.*" I think that, if every family were to follow that biblical advice, we would have a far better world. After all, family is designed to fully produce the God-given potential that resides in all of us. Certainly, my family is a product of that view.

Despite my trying to paint a picture of mostly idyllic peace "of sorts" here just east of what was fast becoming the town of Alice, Texas, I'm afraid that would be an unrealistic image. It remained a rough country. Every day that I rode out on the ranch to check my beeves or journeyed to Corpus Christi to buy and sell livestock, I was on guard against whatever possible trouble might lurk from around a bend in the road or behind some dense motte of mesquite or live oak. My trusty Colt revolver and that Winchester 1873 were near constant companions.

Danger lurked and being prepared to meet it was essential. One day, Andree Ann and I left the children with Clara – she was no longer a slave, mind you, but stayed on as our paid housekeeper – and went for a ride, much as we had done when we first married. I had brought a bottle of wine acquired on a recent trip to Corpus Christi, and Andree Ann had thrown together a picnic meal. We'd headed for a favorite spot near an expanse blanketed with beautiful bluebonnets so far as the eye could see. A field of those flowers is quite something to behold. The word that comes to mind is majestic. I had thought about hitching the buggy, but we'd decided instead to saddle a couple of horses. We packed our picnic into some saddlebags, and off we went. By the way, I may not have shared that Andree Ann – in addition to her great role as a mother and wife – was an excellent horsewoman. Not hitching the buggy would turn out to have been a good decision.

As we trotted along the trail a couple of miles toward our favorite spot near the creek, we rounded a bend and came face to face with three of the scariest characters I ever laid my eyes on. They made Comanche look tame by comparison. By their dress and complexions, they appeared to be Mexicans. The apparent leader sat astride a pale horse. I likely should have mentioned it earlier, but I had a long-held, in-bred prejudice against pale horses, as they reminded me of one of the feared horsemen of the Apocalypse as described in the Book of Revelation. Generally, I had no particular beef with Mexicans. Some of my best ranch hands were of Mexican heritage. They generally made excellent *vaqueros*. These three we were facing were not of that stripe.

"Get behind me!" I half-whispered to Andree Ann. My hand instinctively moved to the butt of my pistol. In that split second, I considered that making a move for my rifle would be too great a risk. I turned my horse sideways to better protect Andree Ann.

"*Aye, hombre! Hola, señora.*" The largest of the three men, the one on the pale horse, offered a greeting that reeked of threat. Through a black toothless smile, he tilted back his head and tacked on, "*Como estas?*"

I actually had the temerity to think for a moment that we might emerge from this unscathed. "*Buenas dias, amigos.*" I tried to be friendly, but made it clear from my tone of voice that I'd be no pushover. They clearly were unaware of who I was and the Dunn prowess with guns and success in fighting Indians and banditos.

"*Tienes dinero?*" They wasted no time asking if we had any money. They wore crossed bandoliers over their vests and sat with their rifles balanced across their saddle horns. I figured I might get one before the others could open fire, but Andree Ann would be in danger. I was also concerned that we were still an easy ride from our home and children. I recalled the warning from the Texas Rangers a few months back. In any case, it would tax my best speculator negotiating skills to get us out of this alive. I felt a bead of sweat roll down my back.

"*Apenas estamos montando. No tenemos dinero.*" I told them we were just out for a ride and had no money. About this time, Andree Ann moved closer, and I saw out of the corner of my eye that she held a pistol in the folds of her dress. That enhanced our odds, but we were still very much in deep trouble.

The larger bandito – clearly, they were not out for the fun of it, so I could think of them as bandits – pointed his rifle in our general direction. "*Desmonter! Ahora!*" He ordered us to dismount. They meant business. One of the trio edged his horse about six feet away from the others to establish a degree of separation. They still hadn't pointed their rifles directly at us. "*Ahora!*"

On foot, we'd be at a distinct disadvantage. I slid my pistol from its holster and without pointing it at them eased forward in my saddle and gave the three of them the toughest look I could come up with. "*No meterse con nosotros.*" Loosely translated, I told them not to fool with us. "*Me llamo Nicholas Dunn.*"

The larger bandito glanced at the others, looking side to side through the dark slits that passed for his eyes. He wasn't quite sure now just who he was messing with. I had the feeling he just might have heard of the fighting reputation of the Dunn family. With his free hand, he slowly wiped a bead of sweat from his own chin. He was clearly beginning to have second thoughts.

I continued to lay a don't-mess-with-me look at them. I couldn't afford to show even a hint of weakness. "*No es un buen día para ti morir.*" I told them it wasn't a good day for them to die.

The leader looked me in the eyes and shrugged thoughtfully. "*Si, señor. Es verdad.*" As if on cue, he nodded to his companions and half grunted, "*Vámonos.*" And the three of them slowly turned their horses and rode away from us and our home.

My bluff – if we were to call it that – had worked.

I glanced over at Andree Ann. I half-expected her to faint, but not my Andree Ann. She smiled, "Well, are we having a picnic or not?"

My, but I couldn't help but love this woman.

And we actually picnicked down at the old creek. We had a lovely afternoon. If I might be so bold, Andree Ann was quite taken with the strength I'd exhibited with the bandits. It did arouse our more carnal instincts. Enough said.

I guess it goes without saying that we never told anyone about our encounter, so you readers are learning of it firsthand. I felt blessed that she had practiced on occasion with the pistol. We'd have made a good team had those banditos made the wrong choice.

The years had been so good to us thus far, and we had high hopes that the Dunn family would continue to flourish here in South Texas. It seemed to be our family destiny.

I was especially pleased that we were a fair distance from what some referred to as civilization. We were still pretty much on the frontier, as that 98th meridian line folks spoke about hadn't moved very far west. I did hear that citizens were taking matters into their own hands in dealing with bandits. They continued to organize those vigilance committees, or vigilantes. They were quite a way north and west of our ranch. From what I learned, folks were frustrated that there weren't enough Rangers and sheriffs, and courtroom judges were becoming too much inclined to let lawbreakers off without punishment. Of course, there was the non-courtroom side of justice, and punishment was swift. There was far too much rustling of livestock by bad characters that tended to operate on the fringes of the frontier. The vigilantes exacted their own brand of justice, not necessarily distinguishing between true desperadoes like John Wesley Hardin or Sam Bass and lesser villains.

FIFTEEN

Bluebonnets & Railroads

You dance with them that brung ya.

Texas-ism

B eautiful bluebonnets. Fields of heavenly blue stretching across the horizon. Blends of sky blue, cerulean, turquoise, and indigo dance before your eyes. Bluebonnets have probably been loved and admired since man first trod the vast Texas prairies. Indigenous Indian tribes wove fascinating folk tales around them. It is said that the Spanish priests establishing their missions in Texas gathered the seeds and grew bluebonnets in the surrounding fields. Of note to you lovers of flowers, the two predominant species of bluebonnets are found growing naturally only in Texas and at no other location in the world. Little wonder that the bluebonnet would eventually become the Texas state flower.

You might recall my description of Andree Ann wearing a beautiful garland of bluebonnets at our wedding. From time to time, a wild bit of romance would seize me, and I'd bring a bouquet of bluebonnets home from working out on the ranch. Andree Ann cottoned to flowers in general, but those bluebonnets were extra special.

So, I've painted a picture of vast fields decked in beautiful flowers. Soon enough, those fields would be crisscrossed with ever more railroads and more wagon roads, as the frontier was conquered and people needed to get places faster and faster. Mail and overland stage routes proliferated, supplementing the railroads. I'm not sure what the image might have been for folks back east. You really had to be here to fully experience the acrid odor of steam locomotives contrasted with the sweet smell of bluebonnets; to hear the grunt of a longhorn bull ready to mate; to experience the noise and action in the breaking of saddle broncs; see laborers in the fields using the cotton gin to harvest the fluffy white gold; to step out on the gallery of your home in the morning to see the sun rise and set on unimaginable vistas.

Andree Ann and I were blessed with two more children, Michael and Agnes ("Aggie"). However, like our dear Annie years earlier, we lost little Aggie before she reached her first birthday. Still, we'd the fortune – the blessing – of raising six sons and daughters on the unforgiving but promising South Texas frontier. The ranch flourished with our longhorns and horses.

As I've shared, it wasn't all necessarily peaceful. I might not have mentioned it earlier, but I was known to have one of those famous Irish tempers. I like to call it "character." I simply was unable to truck with any behavior that smacked of wrongdoing. I recall one day my 15-year-old cousin John was hanging on the fence watching me as I banged away with a pistol at a target to improve my marksmanship. Well, it wasn't really to improve my accuracy with a Colt. I was imagining the target as someone who had done me wrong. Guess I was letting loose with a bit of anger and frustration.

"What are you doin', Mr. Nick?" He always called me that.

I tried for a moment to ignore the question. "John, this ain't none of your business."

"You must have a reason, Mr. Nick."

He wasn't going away. "Someone who claimed to be a friend of mine is suing me. I aim to make it clear that I won't stand for that."

That was about as clear an explanation that I could come up with at the moment.

John cocked his head curiously to one side. I doubt he had the faintest idea what a lawsuit was. "You goin' to shoot him, Mr. Nick?"

I actually was of a mind to shoot my supposed friend and fellow ranchman Tom Gallagher on sight. He put me in quite a towering rage, because he had fenced his land and was suing me for damages just because my *vaqueros* had cut his fence and driven a herd of cattle across his pasture. Barbed wire was, mind you, a new invention at this time, and most ranchers resented how it impacted cattle drives and access to water. Young John's question did sort of dash a bit of cold water on my anger. "Maybe," was the only response I could muster.

John nodded thoughtfully, then innocently offered, "Kin I watch?"

I looked away sheepishly.

As is often the case in these sorts of things, the quarrel passed over, and Tom and I became good friends again. Such was the way of those times. Grudges were an unaffordable luxury. My mother used to say, there was no point in having a hissy fit and stompin' on it. In her infinite wisdom – and the Bible's – it was far better to forgive.

Fenced lands and water access were ever-more a concern for ranchers and farmers alike. That gosh-danged barbed wire was becoming a major challenge. I have to admit that it was an effective way to guard what were called our riparian rights – how water was allocated. In times of drought, protecting precious water was vital to keeping most any ranch. The land was generally pretty arid as it was. Unfortunately, it took a while for cattle to learn to stay away from the barbed wire. Over the first few years of this practice of fencing, we wound up putting down several longhorns that had seriously cut themselves on the barbs. The cuts would get infected with screw worm and kill the poor beasts. I never witnessed it personally, but it was said that a raging bull would charge and knock down a wooden fence, but steer clear of barbed wire. Go figure. Expect the beasts had some sense after all.

Fence wars were another concern. I had my run-in with Tom Gallagher over my *vaqueros* cutting his fence, but fence cutting became a serious problem and all-too-common experience in the mid-1880s. These fence wars were fought mostly between large and small ranchers, pretty much those with plenty of more money to put up fences and those who couldn't afford fencing yet were desperate to get their stock to market as quickly as possible. Some said that the supposed romance of the open range was dead. The Texas Rangers were called in to enforce new laws that made fence cutting a felony. Even carrying fence wire cutters in our saddlebags was against the law.

As to water, I expect we were more fortunate than the folks trying to ranch up in the northern and western reaches of Texas. I'd heard it was terribly dry out there, and ranching and what they called dry-farming were risky undertakings. Even with the dreaded Comanche and Kiowa gone, it was tough beyond that infamous 98th meridian. It was almost impossible to even store water, as it got sucked up in the dry air. Evaporation was our enemy. Andree Ann and the rest of us Dunns felt blessed to live on the northeastern reaches of the Nueces Strip. We had our weather challenges and drought years, but not nearly as bad as those folks up north. At least, we could mostly keep our cisterns full. The advent of the windmill to draw water from deep underground became a contraption few ranchers found they could live without.

To the east, Corpus Christi continued to boom. By 1885, there were some 4,200 residents. The main channel had been dredged to permit access by deep-water ships, and there were three banks, several hotels, an ice factory, and Episcopal, Presbyterian, Methodist, Catholic, and Baptist churches. I should add that the channel dredging didn't help my cousin Patrick in getting his cattle to market, as he now had to herd them onto barges instead of wading them across. Many of the city's streets were paved for the first time, and a street railway system was constructed in 1889. I think the very most important addition was a public water system built in 1893. Up to this time, you can imagine that sanitation was a huge challenge, what with cisterns, outhouses, and roadside ditches. With a booming population and increased commerce, a public water system had become critically important.

The weather remained unpredictable. Dryness would creep up from the south, working its way up from the Rio Grande, expelling its hot breath on the Nueces Strip, and spreading in all directions like a cancer metastasizing over the land. We would make excuses, assuring each other that the rain would be coming soon – maybe next week. We watched as watering holes turned to brown puddles of mud that our livestock would not touch. Our deep wells pumped barely potable water for the livestock troughs and our own cooking. We watched the grasses slowly lose their color, and even the hardy mesquite and live oak struggled to survive. Rattlesnakes, javelina, fox, coyotes, and other wildlife became ever more desperate, and we had to take special care when venturing outside our homes. Even the scorpions grew nasty. My father's farm would see its cotton bloom early, and then produce but a few weakened bolls before withering. We all grumbled, but you learned to live with the dry spells. And there were more dry spells than wet ones. I recall my father sharing the Biblical story of Joseph interpreting the dream of the Egyptian pharaoh to store food in seven good years so as to endure the famine of the next seven years. There was a lot to be said for that parable. We did strive to store food as best we could for the lean years. Eternally optimistic, we always believed that relief from the dryness would come soon. Relief most always did come – or not – mostly not. Try telling a thirsty nearly-1,300-pound longhorn to be patient. Oh, and the wet spells could be devastating, with heavy rains and flash floods wiping out all in their path. If a longhorn wasn't starving, it might find itself drowning. Little wonder that water was big business.

During times of drought in places like Corpus Christi, enterprising folks would fill roly barrels with water from cisterns and sell the water to citizens. A roly barrel was naught but a round barrel hauled along by means of a rope, rolling along as it went. Those roly barrels were a welcome sight to thirsty folks.

I finally sold my big ranch. I really hated to let it go. Bottom line, I wasn't getting any younger, recent periods of drought and flood had a bad economic effect, and as I told my family, "the brush was getting too dense and the mortgage on the land too heavy." As with many ranchers – including the massive King Ranch – drought and the ups and downs of the cattle markets meant occasionally securing additional mortgage debt to make it from one season to another. In 1882, I had acquired 7,000 acres closer to what would very soon become the town of Alice. The land was carved out of an old original Mexican grant gifted to Ynojosa Vital and was called La Anima Sola Tract. Unlike the humble house I originally built, the one that Andree Ann and I had raised our children in, the new house featured those special features that made her especially happy. I even rigged an indoor hand pump so we could have running water inside the main ranch house. Of course, there was a concrete cistern to ensure a reasonably regular water source. There was still an outhouse we would avail ourselves, of mind you. A two-holer, of course.

There was a deep-seated property rights culture that characterized us Texans. As you might imagine, even our more modest acreage required a lot of tending to. New laws against trespass were popping up and along with the fencing was leading to changes in the ranching culture. Cowboys began to find it tougher to get cowhand work; range round-ups and traditional drives disappeared, and they had to turn to laboring at loading pens and chutes. It was mostly work on foot rather than horseback. I for one was determined not to have that be the fate of my *vaqueros*, and I did my best to keep them employed on my ranch, or even lend them out to neighboring ranches.

Times were changing in Texas, as we inevitably progressed from the days of the Colt revolvers and Winchester rifles to railroads to barbed wire to windmills. I heard it called the industrial revolution. By whatever name some highfalutin' dude might call it, there was a sense of bigger things yet to come. Texans – especially we Irish immigrants – had a confidence borne of years of carving successes out of challenging environments.

In the spring of 1885, New Orleans featured a World's Exposition. My father managed to acquire two bushels of Sea Island cotton seed from Dr. William DeRyee at the exposition. My father had raised cotton through the War Between the States but had reduced the crop in the years since. I was growing some cotton of late, and I guess I inspired him. Actually, I was credited with growing a cotton plant on Palito Blanco Creek about 12 miles from San Diego that was supposed to be the largest on record. Planted in 1878, it produced seven crops and measured 7 feet in height and had a 7-inch diameter stalk at its base. That plant required a 13-foot pole to measure its branches side to side. Unfortunately, the vigor of the cotton crops soon faced a great peril, as the boll weevil made its first U.S. appearance at Corpus Christi in 1901. Consequently, we redoubled our efforts at raising beeves, sheep, and horses.

My father, John, Sr., passed away in 1894. Even in death, he seemed larger than life. He had been such a humble, loving, giving soul. He had an infectious optimism that infected everyone around him. Of special note was that I had been told by my father that, even though it wasn't in his will, that it was his intention to change it in order to leave my brother Mike some land on Nueces Bay. My brother John saw to the honoring of our father's request and deeded 60 acres of the Nueces Bay land to Mike. As I've said, we Dunns were a close family, and we honored and loved each other.

At the risk of inflating my prowess at selecting prime livestock, I'm pleased to share a story about an incredible longhorn. Long about 1888, I had taken a considerable liking to a promising young longhorn bull. Having raised and speculated in beeves for so many years, I was a bit optimistic about this bull's potential and boldly named him Champion. He had been calved on a little Mexican ranch down near the Rio Grande and was quite gentle as longhorns went. At only two years of age, Champion already sported a set of horns worthy of a six-year-old.

I did like Champion but, given the speculator in me, I eventually decided to sell him, along with two hundred steers at 12 dollars a head, to a fellow named Sid Grover. Grover bought Champion on behalf of Jim Dobie of the Jim Dobie Ranch near Lagarto in Live Oak County. They soon moved the longhorn to the nearby Kentuck Ranch. Champion's hide was a pale red and brown color. He featured a strong frame and immense horns. The weight of the horns forced him to lower his head, and his head actually wobbled a bit when he walked. His horns curved outward rather than upward. Conveniently, he could scratch the root of his tail with but a slight turn of his head. We figured that Champion's mother was likely a plain Mexican or Texan cow. But due to the fine texture of his hair, we thought his sire must have had a considerable amount of Devon blood in him. We guessed that Champion in his prime weighed in at around twelve hundred pounds. Given that longhorns were not so meaty and profitable as Herefords and other breeds, they were sort of becoming historic critters.

In 1899, Dobie shipped Champion off to the International Fair at San Antonio, along with another bull owned by a fellow named George West to show them off. Champion's picture graced an enameled tin medallion used to promote the event and claimed a horn spread of nine feet.

Will B. Eidson, a South Texas cowboy and world champion roper, took Champion on Dobie's behalf to the 1900 Democratic National Convention. He charged a fee for folks to get a peek at him. Champion didn't attract as much attention as William Jennings Bryan, but receipts were good. It gave Dobie's people pause to imagine that they could make a mint of money, far more than he'd bring at some slaughterhouse. There were plans to take Champion to the Paris Exposition, but they fell apart when the French government expressed unfounded fears of the dreaded "Texas fever."

By 1901, Champion had more than lived up to his name. The "Beeville Bee" newspaper reported a horn spread of seven feet, eight inches – that's 92 inches if you're counting. However, Chicago newspapers in 1900 had reported his horn spread at nine feet and seven inches. To my knowledge, Champion boasted the broadest horn spread of any Texas bull at that time. Keep in mind that the typical horn spreads on longhorns driven north on cattle drives were something under four feet with an occasional five-footer. By my own experience, any spread over six feet was notable.

Jim Dobie leased Champion in 1901 to a wild west show operated by C.Z. Green and his wife. I hear tell that Will Eidson saw him up in Iowa, and Champion seemed to remember the cowboy. They charged two bits to see him, though it was reportedly a losing proposition moneywise. I've been told that he was shown throughout the mid-west, though, and eventually he did meet his end under a butcher's knife in Michigan. Some say that Champion was preserved by a taxidermist and passed into the hands of Miller Brothers 101 Ranch Wild West Show. I have to admit to being fascinated at how folks would pay two bits and get excited by a set of big longhorns with a bull hitched underneath. Go figure.

I'd be remiss here not to mention one of the notable exploits of my son, John Francis Dunn. He was the eighth of our nine children. Let it be said that few fathers could be as proud of their sons as I was of John. He was born in 1870, and I started to teach him the cattle business about the time he could sit a saddle. I also managed to send him off for a bit of education at St Mary's College in San Antonio. He even served the Texas Rangers as a special member thanks to the tracking skills I'd taught him. Before I knew it, he was all grown up and had shifted his attention from teasing his sisters to buying his own ranch near Alice and stocking it with upward of 1,000 Hereford cows and 50 registered bulls.

John's early experiences with the Texas Rangers drew him to San Antonio in 1898 as Teddy Roosevelt was gathering his Rough Riders there for training in preparation for heading off to Cuba. The Rough Riders were officially called the 1st U.S. Volunteer Cavalry. Turned out that the name Rough Riders was a name first used by a news correspondent named Richard Oulahan, and it stuck despite initial protest by Roosevelt.

John was ready to volunteer, joining with men of a broad mix of backgrounds, from nattily dressed eastern college boys to frontiersmen with nicknames like Rocky Mountain Bill, Rattlesnake Pete, Lariat Ned, and Bronco George. John told me he was impressed with Roosevelt who, after an initial stay at the Menger Hotel, camped with his men during their training at Riverside Park. He thought Roosevelt was also a good judge of horseflesh, as he purchased his horse privately to suit his riding preferences rather than accept a standard-issue mount. Ultimately, John decided that his Texas Ranger tracking experience wasn't a fit for the expedition to Cuba. John bade farewell to the Rough Riders. I didn't get the impression that he was reluctant to leave.

John quickly matured to become a successful rancher and tough-minded, no-nonsense businessman. It's not surprising that John found time to serve as a Texas Ranger for several years as a special member of Company E, Frontier Battalion under Captain J.S. McNeill. I expect the Rangers found my son's considerable knowledge of the trails south of the Nueces to the Rio Grande was unmatched. I'd also like to think that my taking him along on my travels around the Nueces Strip to hunt and make livestock deals contributed to his storehouse of knowledge.

★

One day long about 1903, my dear cousin John Hillard Dunn dropped by. With the job market seemingly unstable at best, John had decided to take my advice and work for himself. He settled on getting into the railroad business. He came home and bought four teams and the equipment for a grading outfit – all on credit. Work had begun on the construction of a new rail line from Robstown to Brownsville, part of the St. Louis, Brownsville & Mexico Railroad. He hired some men and a smallish Negro cook named Kinkey Joe. John worked for a couple of weeks for a railroad contractor, grading roadbeds just south of Robstown at $3.00 a day for team and driver. Then, he got a contract on his own for two miles of grading where the town of Sarita would later spring up.

As he told it, the new line was going to be the first railroad to reach Brownsville, Texas. It was to be built across vast ranches: Driscoll's, King's, Kennedy's, and Armstrong's from Robstown to Harlingen. But those places were only names on a railroad map at the time; the inhabitants had pretty much not yet actually arrived. On that 100 miles, there was only one house in sight from the railroad right-of-way. Such was the vastness and potential of the frontier. Towns thrived or died depending on whether the railroad right-of-way went through them or bypassed them. Visionary and influential men were setting the stage for Texas' future.

According to John, along the 40 miles from Harlingen to Brownsville, the rail line crossed fertile black-land prairies, brush land, sandy desert, and then more brush. From Raymondville, he helped build a branch line to Sam Fordyce through heavy brush, a part of which is now called "Magic Valley," where 200,000 people would eventually replace the coyotes and the cattle. The wheels – or rather rails – of progress had been set in motion in South Texas. Economic winners and losers were being created with every mile of track laid.

Until railroad building got underway in Texas, most commerce tended to be around waterways and coastal areas. I recall my grandfather Long Larry teaching me how early civilizations developed around coasts and waterways so as to facilitate commerce and travel. Moreover, traveling over land placed travelers at greater risk for robbers or worse. It was hardly different in 19th century Texas. Overland travel entailed teams of horses or oxen pulling heavily laden carts. You may recall my father's wagon trains, as I described earlier, with each wagon bursting at the seams with cotton and being pulled by a slow plodding 16-horse team down to Vera Cruz, Mexico. It was labor-intensive, fraught with risk, and time-consuming. This problem of quickly, efficiently, and affordably transporting goods to market was acute to say the least. With the evolution of practical locomotives, the stage was set for an era of new railroad line construction throughout the Nueces Strip. There was also considerable repair work needed on existing lines. While Texas railroads emerged with little overt damage from the War Between the States, most equipment was suffering from general wear and tear by the time hostilities closed, combined with general disuse in the couple of decades following.

There was a science of sorts to building railroads. Most folks have images of long lines of workers laying wooden ties, placing steel rails, and securing them by hammering in spikes. There was much more to it than that. Geography and topography were critically important. Designers and engineers sought to always take the paths of least resistance. While most of the plains areas of South Texas were flat, there were occasional elevation changes of as much as 100 feet. The lowest possible, often longest grade was most desirable, as short steep grades were far more difficult for a locomotive. A slow-moving train struggling up a steep grade was also a sitting duck for train robbers. In addition to grading, railroad construction took more resources to lay track across rivers, arroyos, and ravines where bridges were required. Of course, during heavy rainfall, rivers would flood their banks and could heavily damage or even wipe out the bridges. Flash floods were a lurking danger during especially heavy rains.

Importantly, the railroads afforded economic access. Millions of citrus trees, miles of winter vegetables, and acres of cotton eventually would take the place of the brush and cactus that covered the sections where the railroads were built. When one part of a line was completed, John moved farther north to help build the line up close to Houston. John's brother Joe soon joined him, and the business became known as Dunn Brothers Grading Contractors. They had built up a 12-team outfit as business thrived.

John moved on to Sinton, Texas, in Refugio County where he had a contract for eight miles of grading between Sinton and the Nueces River. From Sinton, he moved to the next job at Vanderbilt, which was just another name on the map at that time. Vanderbilt was 14 miles from the depot at Edna, so John shipped their outfit by train to Edna. They had to stay there for three days because heavy rains made the roads impassable. The irony of dealing with impassable roads while trying to build a railroad wasn't lost on John.

John loved to tell me about meeting his future wife, Stella. Edna, Texas was a little town of about 400 people, including some very attractive girls. One of the best-looking and most attractive was Stella Grissom. She was a tall girl by standards of the day at about 5-feet, 4 inches tall with dark auburn hair and grey come-hither eyes. Stella was a graceful dancer and a good companion on the buggy rides they took for picnics. Before John moved on to his next job, he proposed, gave her a diamond ring, and asked her to wait until he made $50,000. As the story goes, there was a certain amount of swagger, as he never delivered on the money pledge but eventually would marry Stella.

Dunn Brothers moved on to Grimes County to help build the Trinity & Brazos Valley Railway from Houston to Fort Worth. Their Mexican laborers quit them at Edna, with the exception of a fellow named Tim Castilla. They said they would not go so far north of the Rio Grande. The white natives John employed were a worthless bunch, and they would not permit Negroes on the job because of recent race riots. Finally, they consented to permit Dunn Brothers to import some Negroes from Madison, but later decided to run them out. John bought 20-gauge, double-barrel shot guns with plenty of shells as sort of an insurance policy and kept the Negroes on the job until it was finished. A mob of about a dozen white men formed one night aiming to chase John, Joe, and the Negroes away. As John tells it, the confrontation went down pretty much as follows:

John and Joe were aroused from their bunks by Bo Butler, one of the Negro crew leaders. Alerted by the noise outside, they threw caution to the winds and ran as fast as they could to the camp to head off the trouble. They quickly positioned themselves between the Negro encampment and the troublemakers.

Now comes the best part of John's story. The men stopped when John – picture him with a pair of pistols in his belt and a double-barrel shotgun in each hand – stepped from the shadows. Joe – equally well-armed – emerged from about 20 feet away. "Where do you fellas think you're goin'?" They tried to sound as commanding as possible. The troublemakers likely had not expected resistance. Recall that it didn't exactly hurt that the Dunn family had built a reputation in South Texas for toughness.

The apparent leader, Colt Smith, was nudged reluctantly forward by the mob. "Um…we aim to chase them Nigras outta here." He stood looking downward. He knew better than to look John in the eye.

John and Joe pointed the shotguns at the ground. John softened his voice to seem more persuasive. "Colt, Colt…now, you folks have had some great fun drinking an' carryin' on tonight." He tried to sound reasonable but firm. "Surely you don't want to start trouble that might not end well for you."

The mob grumbled and urged Colt Smith to lead them forward. He finally glanced upward with his head sort of sideways. "No disrespect for you, John, but we've had enough o' them Nigras." He was still 15 feet or so away but took a hesitant step toward John and Joe. That wasn't such a good idea.

The air was shattered by a blast from one of John's shotguns. The mob froze. The shotgun had blown a good-size crater in the earth a couple of feet in front of Colt. "Don't you men go doin' something' stupid." John gave them one of those dead serious, don't-mess-with-me, penetrating stare downs. John liked to think that his steely blue eyes dared the mob to make trouble. There was an unearthly silence, quiet enough to hear mosquito wings beating the air.

After a few more interminably long seconds, there was more grumbling and murmuring, as the mob reluctantly began to disperse. John and Joe took turns keeping watch for the next couple of hours. They sat outside with those shotguns cradled in their laps.

John admitted to me that he was actually a little disappointed that no one seriously challenged Joe and him. The shotgun blast into the dirt was the only shot fired.

Distractions like mobs aside, Dunn Brothers' work on building Texas railroads went on pretty much uneventfully. The biggest challenge was most often the weather.

To hasten construction of the system toward becoming operational, Uriah Lott had acquired the San Antonio, Chapin & Rio Grande Railway and the San Benito & Rio Grande Valley Railway.

Soon enough, the Dunn railroad business began to go broke for lack of consistent new work. It began with selling a couple of rigs. Finally, the brothers sold out, paid their debts, settled with the work crews, and headed to New Orleans and the Mardi Gras celebration before heading home. The Dunn brothers knew hard work as well as how to have a good time. It was a sort of life balance. In New Orleans, John learned about how the United States had taken over canal building from the French at the Isthmus of Panama, and now they were seeking able men. John parlayed his railroad experience into what would be a career spanning several years helping with building the Panama Canal. He would face tremendous challenges in the heat and the fetid jungles of Panama, but it wouldn't stop him from marrying Stella and having two sons and a daughter.

John stopped by on one of his visits home from Panama long enough to share a bit of background with me about the Canal. John knew I appreciated history. He told me how the Isthmus of Panama was explored by Columbus in 1502 and crossed by Balboa in 1513. Balboa founded the town of Panama in 1519. Much like the shores of South Texas, Panama would be home to all manner of pirates, brigands, and buccaneers, including the infamous pirate Morgan. After nearly two centuries had passed, Spain decided to build a canal – but nothing was done. In 1848, the Granada government gave a Mr. Aspinwall from New York a railroad concession. In spite of the terrible death rate due to malaria and yellow fever, the railway was built. It started at Colon and ended at Panama. It opened for traffic in 1855 and was the first and only workable inter-oceanic route since the Spanish Trail until the Canal was completed.

In between, the French formed a company to build the Canal in 1879 but, after a decade, work ground to a halt, thanks mostly to disease that sapped manpower. The French company offered to sell the business to the United States, but Colombia – of which Panama was a province – refused to ratify a treaty with the United States. President Theodore Roosevelt made short work of their resistance when he sent the U.S. warship Nashville to Colon. The next day, the Republic of Panama was born with the loss of only one life.

John and I eventually met up in Corpus Christi in 1908 on one of his trips back to the states. He and Stella treasured the time away from the heat and humidity of Panama. John told me of several brushes he had with danger during his work on the Canal, as he led several crews working with dynamite to make the cuts required for the Canal. John's experience with railroads in Texas came in right handy – especially dealing with laborers. As he described it: "By the end of 1906, the yellow fever had disappeared, although malaria continued. Labor was the next problem. Skilled workers were recruited almost exclusively from among the Americans, but in addition there was a veritable army of manual laborers. These were of various types, but mostly blacks. They were paid in different kinds of money. The first were called the gold force, because they were paid in gold dollars, and the second as the silver force, which was paid in local currency. Panama had a deplorable reputation – it was necessary to offer exceptional advantages in order to attract the white race. The salaries were 25 percent to 100 percent above what they would have earned in the United States. Also, they had living quarters thrown in for free. They had six weeks of annual holiday with pay! The company owned the commissaries, so it's no surprise that goods were extremely low cost. An excellent gold force of 5,000 men was built up as a result.

"The natives were quite useless, being entirely indifferent and shiftless. West Indian Negroes were brought in. They were lazy, vain, and their output very low. On the other hand, the Spaniards from northern Spain, when they were reinforced by Italians, Greeks, and a few Frenchmen, soon created an efficient nucleus. During the period of active construction, there were 45,000 workers on the Canal, of whom 30,000 were blacks and 12,000 were Europeans – the latter figure including 8,000 Spaniards."

The yellow fever mosquitoes had been nearly eradicated thanks to Dr. William Gorgas, who figured out they carried the disease and bred prolifically in the decorative pottery placed around Panama Canal living quarters years earlier by the French. Up to then, scientists and physicians attributed the disease to what I described earlier as "miasma" or toxic air.

John noted that premature detonation of dynamite was of the gravest concern. On more than one occasion, dozens were killed by mis-timed explosions. One time, John was helping supervise some blasting aimed at breaking up large rocks to facilitate their removal. They placed a "dobie" – five to fifteen sticks of dynamite covered with a pile of mud – on each rock along with a two-foot fuse. One day, the "dobies" were not correctly fused, and John barely escaped harm as a massive series of explosions rocked the work site and killed several men. I couldn't help but admire John's dedication and his luck. Once the Panama Canal was completed, he moved Stella and his children to the American Midwest and returned to enjoying a railroad career.

I shared John Hillard Dunn's experiences with the Panama Canal not simply because they illustrated the toughness and determination of the Dunn family and Texans in general, but to share the many cultures that contributed to the Canal building, just as diverse nationalities had contributed to the development of South Texas. It was a remarkable undertaking to blend all these peoples toward a common though unarticulated goal of forging a civilization.

I should add here that back in 1906 my brother Michael founded the Dunn Grocery Company in Corpus Christi. Entrepreneurship seemed to run in our family. It became a thriving concern.

By now, I was feeling the aches and pains of a youth spent droving cattle, fighting Indians, breaking horses, and herding longhorns. Several of our children were now adults and looking to raise families of their own. John F. married a sweet young girl named Mary Crain. My dear daughter Maggie, who learned to love those horny toads, married a handsome fellow named Frank Evans by whom she would give me six grandchildren. Dominic, Mary, Theresa, and Michael would also marry. Andree Ann and I were truly gifted to see God's blessing on family, to see our Texas destiny being fulfilled.

SIXTEEN

End of the Trail

Life's too short not to have lived it as a Texan.

Texas-ism

In 1906, I had reached the ripe old age of 71 and had to have one of my legs amputated above the knee owing to a lingering infection. I had uncharacteristically fallen from a horse. That was a nasty business. The image of a doctor cutting flesh and sawing through bone was not appealing to me in the least way. Of course, it didn't slow me down much.

I continued to drive my buggy with two lively horses and even rode horseback when necessary. I always loved my horses. Occasionally, Andree Ann and I would embark on one of our special picnics. While grateful to have no further encounters with banditos, we always went well-armed just in case. We could still hit just about anything we aimed a gun at.

Importantly, in September 1906, I received my official U.S. Government-issued Certificate of Citizenship. My cousin Pat Whelan was one of the witnesses. It had taken me a long time to get around to making me an official American, though I had to think of myself as a Texan first and foremost.

When the families – especially my grandkids – visited, I'd regale the little ones with recollections of cattle drives, breeding cattle and horses, battling banditos, and fighting Comanche. Many of my fondest tales involved my beloved horses, and the best stories invariably included that black stallion Thunder that I owned back when I courted Andree Ann and began raising our family. Thunder had seen some dangerous action while I dealt with banditos and Comanche. My son John still had those Comanche arrows including Nellie's, mementos lovingly preserved over the years. As I thought back on it, the family had seen more than its fair share of danger helping conquer the South Texas frontier.

I did still have a quick, impulsive disposition, though most would say it was coupled with a kind heart. Due to my early church moral training, I never – except for Comanche – killed anyone, though I admittedly threatened and frightened a few. One day not too long after the operation on my leg, I was standing outside a pen where my horses were being worked. One of the *vaqueros* started to abuse a horse. You know how much I loved horses, and I would never tolerate mistreatment of any kind. I'm sort of embarrassed to admit that I yelled at that *vaquero* something like, "If I could climb this fence, I would go out there and beat your head off with my crutch," – not realizing in the heat of the moment that I very likely could not stand on one leg while using the crutch for a club. My anger quickly subsided to a grin as I realized the predicament I'd have been in. To his credit, the *vaquero* must have recognized his near-brush with violence, apologized, and didn't mistreat any more horses.

I found myself continuing to deal with that pesky infection in my leg. It was slowing down my aging body, though I was ever alert and of good humor.

Well, my life is pretty much getting to be history now. It's Texas history as descended from a visionary Irishman and his beautiful wife, grandparents that I loved and cherished the memory of. I had known in my heart that, when I left County Kildare, I'd never see them again. Long Larry Dunn and Ellen O'Reilly Dunn had indeed produced and

NICHOLAS DUNN–TEXAS LEGEND

enabled a Texas family destiny. I felt assured that, when my time to meet the Lord came, I could rest easy that the descendants of Long Larry would populate and help grow South Texas for decades to come, leaving a lasting imprint on Texas history.

230

SOURCES

The following materials served as factual sources upon which most of *Nicholas Dunn: The Making of a Texas Legend* was based.

My Family as I Knew Them, John Hillard Dunn, Corpus Christi, 1952, On file at Library of The University of Texas Institute of Texan Cultures at San Antonio

Perilous Trails of Texas, by J. B. (Red) John Dunn, ©1932, JB John Dunn, Southwest Press

Celtic Trails of Texas, John Meaney ©1984, John W. Meaney

The Irish Texans, by John Brendan Flannery, ©1980 John Flannery, The University of Texas Institute of Texan Cultures at San Antonio

Texas-The Country and Its Men, by Lewis E. Daniell (Austin TX, ©1924).

Ellis A. Davis and Edwin H. Grobe, comps., *The New Encyclopedia of Texas* (4 vols. Dallas: Texas Development Bureau, 1929)

A Vaquero of the Brush Country, by J. Frank Dobie, University of Texas Press, ©1929, 2nd printing ©1985

Cow People, by J. Frank Dobie, ©1964, 4th printing ©1990, University of Texas Press.

REFLECTIONS FROM THE DUNN FAMILY TREE

Nicholas Dunn: The Making of a Texas Legend, should be a staple of every true Texan's library. Author Mark Greathouse brings to life the adventures of my great grandfather in an action-packed biography. He's captured the full spirit of the man from 15-year-old Irish lad landing in Corpus Christi in 1850 through his life as cattle drover, rancher, defender against Comanche and bandits, and man of family and faith. Being a rancher, I fully appreciate this first-person tale of my ancestor carving a life on the vast and unforgiving prairies of the Nueces Strip.

> – John F. Dunn, Rancher, 5th Generation Texan, and Great Grandson of Nicholas Dunn

While Richard King was building an empire, Nicholas Dunn was building a life, a ranch, a family, and a good name in that same part of Texas where the "wild west" never died. It just went to sleep and every so often reawakens. Author Mark Greathouse has undertaken that reawakening, as he takes the time to set the table for a feast of true stories about a South Texas pioneer that was about as colorful as they come.

> – James Holmgreen, Great Great Grandson to Nicholas Dunn

I found myself fully captivated by author Mark Greathouse's bringing to life the adventures of my great grandfather in an action-packed, history-laced epic. Readers will fully sense the mix of Irish brogue and Texas twang in this first-person tale of Nicholas Dunn raising his family and carving a life on the harsh prairies of the Nueces Strip, becoming by any measure a Texas legend.

> – MaryAnne Dunn Bose, 5th Generation Texan and Great Granddaughter to Nicholas Dunn

My Uncle Nick was an unforgettable character. He not only raised cattle on his 20,000-acre ranch near Alice, Texas, he was a speculator buying and selling cattle. He would have been at home as a stockbroker on Wall Street. Uncle Nick had a quick, impulsive disposition and a kind heart. I valued his advice.

– John Hillard Dunn (1883 – 1958), Entrepreneur, Railroad Man, and Nephew to Nicholas Dunn

Confession time. In writing the life story of my great great grandfather, a biography if you will, I made a decision to choose the first person. Thus, *Nicholas Dunn: The Making of a Texas Legend* is a biography disguised as an autobiography. To me, describing his life in the first person made it far more interesting, creating a personalization designed to generate a sort of magnetic attraction or ephemeral allure. Moreover, this work is also of the historical western fiction genre in the sense that dialog and more detailed descriptions of scenes long ago lost to memory or only cursorily described have been created such that readers and listeners might better experience the Dunn family adventures. Make no mistake, as I stated in Nick's voice early on, "mind you that I don't truck with embellishment. No, not me. Some folk think we Irish tend to exaggerate. What I share with you is true… as I remember it. No blarney." No blarney indeed. And as can be seen from the assembled reference sources, there's quite a bit backing up this tale of the life of Nicholas Dunn.

I defined a "legend" early on as "an extremely famous or notorious person, especially in a particular field or endeavor; a person who inspires legends." Was Nicholas Dunn truly a legend? A Texas legend? Damn right! He never graced the pages of any exaggerated dime store novels of his era, as he was a humble hero to all who knew him. He was a man who immigrated to Texas as a teenager and made a life grounded in fully understanding the psychological nature of longhorns and horses. He was brave enough to take on and defeat savage Comanche. As a young man, Nicholas Dunn quickly developed the powers of observation, alertness, loyalty and, most importantly, resourcefulness essential to the ranching profession. In addition, he'd developed critically important skills such as excellent marksmanship and horsemanship. He was considered intelligent, shrewd, hard-working, and of high moral character by family, friends, and community. In sum, he was legendary, having lived life head and shoulders above most men of his time.

Nicholas Dunn passed away August 29, 1912 in Alice, Texas at age 77. He was buried in Holy Cross Cemetery, Corpus Christi, Texas in the cemetery of Sacred Heart of Jesus Church. Andree Ann passed away December 24, 1929 in Beeville, TX and is buried close by her beloved husband in Corpus Christi. A memorial marker stands to their memory.

Nicholas' son John married Mary Crain in January 1915. She was the daughter of former Congressman William Henry Crain of Cuero, Texas. John and Mary would have five children. John's two great loves were his family and his herds of cattle. Following in the family tradition, he took an active part in the civic affairs of the town of Alice and of Jim Wells County. John would pass away in 1948 at age 78, having maintained a long-standing reputation epitomizing the successful Texas ranchers and businessmen of the era.

John exemplified the reputation for toughness and honest dealings for which the Dunn family became known throughout South Texas. An example of this occurred in the mid-1920s. Among properties he owned in Alice, Texas, John owned an interest in the Citizens State Bank at Alice. This son of Nicholas Dunn was tough, as they say, a chip off the old block. According to several witnesses, he was standing in the bank one day leaning against a counter with his right foot up on a brass foot rail. Keep in mind that John was a tall man, having inherited his great grandfather Long Larry's height. The incident went something like this.

An itinerant with a grudge against John strode into the bank and walked up to him. "You sonofabitch, you an yur bank ru-int my life!" And he kicked John's foot off the rail.

It was said that at that split-second of silence you could have easily cut the air inside that bank like soft butter with a dull hot knife. Without hesitation, John let loose with a single punch that separated the man from several of his front teeth and dropped him to the floor.

Upon standing back to assess the damage and dust himself off, John noticed that one of his cufflinks was missing. Without uttering a word, he proceeded to grab the beaten man by the scruff of his neck and lead him around the floor until the cufflink was found. By this time the intruder, with blood all over his face and dirt ground into his elbows and knees from scrounging around the floor of the bank, was more or less coming to. John unceremoniously dragged him to the front door and kicked the man out of the bank. It had been an amazing performance.

Here's where this story takes a fascinating turn. The beaten man happened to be a Ku Klux Klan member. He dragged himself off and complained to the Klan, asking that they tar and feather this man who had beaten him up. When the itinerant told the Klansmen it was John Francis Dunn that had whipped him, the Klan wanted no part of the incident. Such was the reputation for toughness of the Dunn family in South Texas.

Notably, the Ku Klux Klan never achieved the sort of notoriety in Texas as it apparently had in other parts of the South. It had been organized back around 1868, coincident with Reconstruction, by a fellow named Roger Mills. Mills happened to be a member of the Democratic Party that was striving to fend off the carpetbagging Republicans that were sweeping elections throughout the south. The Klan mostly used acts of intimidation like stealing horses, conducting a few lynchings, and burning crops to intimidate folks with Republican political leanings. They held no love for the opportunistic carpetbaggers. Authorities soon clamped down hard on the Klan and they were nearly nonexistent by 1870. The Texas legislature even passed a measure making it illegal to be armed and disguised with a hood. Then Governor Edmund Davis called for formation of a militia or a state police to further clamp down on possible Ku Klux Klan activity. Bottom line, the Klan mentioned in my tale of John Dunn likely didn't amount to much, especially as they had a resurgence in the early 1900s that didn't match up with their past depredations.

By way of further illustrating the impact of the Dunn family in South Texas, it's worthwhile here to note how Nicholas Dunn's cousin Patrick Dunn's ranching venture on North Padre Island turned out. Patrick's house was destroyed in the hurricane of 1916, so he replaced it with a smaller one. Eventually, he sold his holdings – except for grazing rights – on Padre Island to Colonel Sam Robertson, who intended to develop the island as a tourist attraction. The ranch portion continued in the family under the management of Patrick's son, Burton, who kept the ranch operations going until his own death in 1970. Today, most of the 110-mile long Padre Island is a national seashore. Well to its south lies the Texas tourist mecca, South Padre Island (Sam Robertson's island resort vision was apparently a bit too far north). Notably, to the end of his days, Patrick regretted selling the island. He equated the island to a sense of freedom not to be found on the mainland, much less anywhere else on earth. I think Patrick really captured the essence of life in South Texas. It was about freedom.

"Red John" Dunn owned and operated that impressive museum of military artifacts on the outskirts of Corpus Christi. In 1932, he published a book about his exploits in South Texas titled *Perilous Trails of Texas*. His daughter Mary Maude (pseud. Lilith Lorraine) was a famed poetess, science fiction writer, and suffragette. She edited "Red John's" book. "Red John," another prototypical Texan, passed away in 1940 at the ripe age of 89. Mary Maude married a cowboy from Falfurrias, Texas named Cleveland Wright; thus, her married name was Mary Maude Dunn Wright. Parts of "Red John's" collection of artifacts can be found today in the Corpus Christi Museum of Science and History

Unsurprisingly, historical markers chronicling the Dunn family are posted throughout the Nueces Strip. Family reunions have brought together hundreds of descendants. At last count, a Dunn family tree I compiled was comprised of more than 2,300 Texas descendants of Long Larry Dunn across nine generations.

Nicholas Dunn: The Making of a Texas Legend was inspired by various Dunn family writings. Back in 1952, my great uncle John Hillard Dunn – of railroad and Panama Canal fame – filed a certified narrative of the Dunn family history with the University of Texas at San Antonio, Libraries Special Collections, Institute of Texan Cultures. John H. Dunn's writings vividly described the lives of the progeny of Long Larry Dunn of County Kildare, Ireland. My Dad – John Francis Greathouse – passed a copy of it along to me about 50 years ago, and I finally transcribed it from shop-worn copy to digital format back in 2012. It was in the process of that task that it struck me how worthy it would be to tell the Dunn family story as an historical biographical novel in the context of South Texas history. While most of the later material in the referenced narrative was about John Hillard Dunn's career, I chose to personalize the tale to me and my own Texas roots. That perspective readily lent itself to vividly telling this tale of forging lives on the often-hostile frontier of South Texas.

My father was so respectful of the family legacy and he harbored such a heartfelt need to pass it to his children that he painstakingly and lovingly hand-copied the Dunn family tree down from the lineage of Lawrence "Long Larry" Dunn. That family tree unlocked all manner of stories. By way of example, one of those stories was that my grandfather, Horace Charles Greathouse, served as a Texas Ranger in 1920. I first became aware of Horace's service during a trip with my cousin Jim Holmgreen to the Heritage Museum down in Falfurrias a few years ago, where a patient and friendly volunteer curator endured my slow digging through the exhibits. There, I came upon my grandfather in an old photo of a Texas Ranger troop, and his name was listed on an accompanying roster and card file. I imagined him a less than reliable fellow, however, as his year of Ranger service coincided with his leaving my grandmother Alma. She remarried, and her second husband – a fellow named Clarence Dalley – moved her and her son (my father) to New York City. Grandma Alma passed away in 1940. She was only 46 years old. Alma was a beautiful lady.

Meanwhile, Grandfather Horace would go to work for the Customs Service in Shreveport, Louisiana, marry twice more, and father two more children before he died in 1957.

Lastly, and truth be told, I didn't need to do much embellishing of Nicholas Dunn's story. It was written that my great-great-grandfather "became widely known as a rancher and cattleman, operated a freight line before the days of the railroads, and was also known as an intrepid and fearless Indian fighter." No more was written of a freight line, but most of Nick's life revolved around ranching and livestock. There's no question that he harbored an entrepreneurial spirit. Life was indeed wild and often violent in the evolving west, especially in the South Texas frontier within the nearly 80-year period to which I confined this story. Rustlers, banditos, Comanche, Apache, yellow fever, wars, rogue soldiers, outlaws, politics, cattle drives, round-ups, and more were part and parcel to life in that era. Layer onto that the very nature of the terrain and unpredictably rough weather, and it deepens one's appreciation for the hardiness and commitment demanded of those who settled the frontier.

The Dunn family actually did experience all of the happenings described within these pages of *Nicholas Dunn: The Making of a Texas Legend*. While most of the stories John Hillard Dunn passed along are from verbal accounts, most events are able to be corroborated by eye witnesses, including "Red John" Dunn's own writings in *Perilous Trails of Texas*, the writings of a cousin John W. Meaney in *Celtic Trails of Texas,* and by various newspaper articles and historical accounts.

Aside from the inherent challenges of frontier life, there were many joyous contributions to what became a large family imprint on the soul of Texas. The Dunns were a generous, family- and faith-oriented lot. They donated many of their land holdings to the local parishes of the Catholic Church. Successful ranching and businesses, lots of children, weddings, marriages, and active participation in the life, faith, and politics of the region were woven into the fabric of my family – Irish Texans – the heirs of Long Larry Dunn. To this day, some descendants of Long Larry still live and work on lands handed down through the family generation by generation. Indeed, a Texas family destiny. The enduring nature of their lives give credence to considering Nicholas Dunn a true Texas legend.

It's easy to forget that a mere 160 years ago, our nation was struggling in the ongoing throes of its own westward evolution. It was an experiment in the sanctity of the citizens running the government, not the other way around. Fueled by politics, economics, faith, and emotion-laden moral and social issues, the people of the United States of America were forging what would become the enduring legacy of an exceptional nation. The pioneers settling the Texas frontier surely exemplify this incredible dynamic. Folks dare not too easily forget the hard work, the endurance, and sacrifices of our forebearers. Importantly, Nicholas Dunn's story shares the critical importance of the family in the building of the United States, especially the ultimate taming of the frontier.

This book offers a snapshot by which readers can vicariously experience life on that American frontier and the building of the American dream. Readers need simply delve deeply into their imaginations, transport themselves to this era, and let their visions run wild with the taming of South Texas. Such must have been the vision that Long Larry Dunn shared with his children and especially instilled in his grandson, Nicholas Dunn. Nicholas immigrated on blind faith, winding up trusting the assurances of his kin to settle in South Texas and then profoundly influencing Texas through the hopes, dreams, and hard work of he and his family. Legend was bred into the very bones of these Irish immigrants, and Nicholas was no exception.

In closing, I take you back to the final stanza of my poem that I shared at the beginning of this book about these kin of Kildare:

> Yet, these kinfolk of County Kildare, these
> staunch Irishmen endured.

They sowed and reaped and made life anew despite all the strife;
Their blood flows crimson in my children's veins.
And the green heathers of County Kildare will ever remember
The sons of Long Larry Dunn.
And so it was with these kin of Kildare; now ya hear.

THE END AND GOD BLESS

Made in the USA
Monee, IL
28 June 2021